TICKLED
IMAGINATION

A TEENAGER'S REALITY
LIVING WITH UNDIAGNOSED
LYME DISEASE

LAUREN KINGSLY

Tickled Imagination:
A Teenager's Reality Living With Undiagnosed Lyme Disease

Copyright © 2019 by Lauren Kingsly

Contact: tickledimagination@gmail.com

ISBN: 978-0-578-22688-0

This book is dedicated to young adults living with a chronic illness. *You are _not_ alone.*

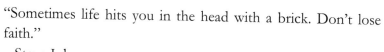

"Sometimes life hits you in the head with a brick. Don't lose faith."
— Steve Jobs

"In utter loneliness a writer tries to explain the inexplicable."
— John Steinbeck

For Mom and Dad,
my best friends and biggest supporters; thank you for never giving up on me.

To Dr. Gedroic,
my "superhero"; thank you for saving me from the yard of sleeping souls

INTRODUCTION

THE THREE QUESTIONS

WHY?

Throughout my long journey with illness, I was asked repeatedly, "Why did you want to write a book when you've endured so much?" I can't say that I have a definitive answer to this question, as many reasons led me to decide to publish my experience.

The first reason was most definitely Him (not the one you'll meet later on). The little boy sitting in a treatment room screaming in terror as several nurses and my doctor tried to thread a PICC line up his arm. I stood paralyzed by the memory of my past, in which I cried out in pain for people in white coats to help me instead of putting me through even more agony.

Seeing the little boy in distress made me understand the gravity of sharing my story. I wanted to impart the knowledge I now possess to other young adults currently enduring illness. I'm hopeful this allows them to feel acknowledged and validated, something I craved throughout my three-year experience. I wished to tell the little boy that, although painful, his journey will come to light and that he *will* feel better.

HOW?

The second most frequent question I received was, "How were you able to compile your thoughts and journal them when going through treatment?" My book began as a series of audio clips I recorded of myself rambling about treatment, fears, hopes, and dreams. About a month after I first visited Dr. Gedroic, I started recording myself to make sure that if I were to lose my mental capacities, I'd have clips to jog my memory. In total, I had 168 audio clips. Although slow at first, by mid-October 2018, I wrote out a page a day until I had reached my planned stopping point. I removed many details, as I'm sure you would not have picked up this book if it were 800+ pages. Also, some information is still a little too close to my heart to divulge, but maybe someday in the future, when I have closure from this chapter in my life, I will. If I mentioned you in this book, our memory is immense, and I felt my story wouldn't be complete without it. To those not included, please do not take offense. My mind was, well, scattered.

WHEN?

This question came in various forms, but all centered around when I believed I first became sick. I hid a lot of my symptoms from my parents, teachers, coaches, and boyfriend at the time. Much to their dismay now, I felt it was necessary to keep my hallucinations and the other cognitive issues I faced un-der wraps. Now I realize that this viewpoint stemmed from my illness, but I do not regret it. I'm thankful for all the twists and turns of my journey as it led me to where I am now, and I couldn't be happier (or healthier). In answer to the question, my symptoms first began during the spring of my sophomore year. What a ride it has been since then.

PART ONE

"No great mind has ever existed without a touch of madness."

– Aristotle

1

It all started with *him*. When I woke up, he was sitting near my bed in my blush-pink, straight-backed chair. Although it would be alarming to most, I found his presence ominous, yet familiar. The moonlight highlighted his silhouette, framing and outlining his rigid face. I caught glimpses of his blonde hair as the light from passing cars shone brightly into my room. He seemed amused that I was confused by his presence.

Struggling to sit up, I glanced over at the alarm clock on my nightstand to read the time. 3:51 am. I leaned back against my headboard, and as my eyes adjusted to the darkness, his appearance became more evident.

Noticing my increased alertness, he fidgeted in the chair and leaned forward, his mouth pursed and his eyes focused as if to speak. I leaned towards him, too, anticipating words would begin to flow from his mouth. Flattered by my enthusiasm, he leaned back, crossed his legs, and smirked. Without turning his head, his eyes flashed in my direction.

"Who are you?" I demanded.

Annoyance consumed his aura. Without hesitation, he turned to face me directly and smirked.

"I think we both know who I am," he said, and his head returned to its former position.

I felt as though my heart would leap out of my chest at any moment, but I could not let him see my nervousness.

"I do not know who you are!" I replied.

His blue eyes turned and locked with mine as he stood and approached the end of my bed. Towering over me, he placed his hands in his pockets and snarled.

"Lauren, just shut up!"

"How do you know my name?!" I exclaimed.

His smirk became a smile. My angry reaction amused him. Then, without another word, he vanished.

I screamed for my mom, beads of sweat rolling down my face. She frantically burst through my door, and I experienced a mixture of paranoia and fury, wondering why she would let a strange man into my room. Little did I know this was the first of many visits to come.

2

After our first encounter, I dismissed his presence by blaming it on a lack of sleep or dehydration. I couldn't come to grips with why he appeared, but I recalled friends mentioning that after they pulled an all-nighter to study, they were frightened by the hallucinations that followed. Zoey, a basketball player who had been recruited by a Division I school, told me once that after she had studied until 4:00 am for her AP Physics exam, she saw her future basketball coach on the eraser head of her pencil. Every time she would use the eraser, her coach would lose part of his body, depending on how much work she had erased.

Acknowledging this, I promised myself that I would drink 64 ounces of water each day and go to bed no later than 11:00 pm.

I hadn't been as diligent with my self-care in the past few weeks, however. Junior year was around the corner, and preparing for the SAT, ACT, and SAT II subject tests consumed my days. So when I saw him sitting there in my room, I figured this was my body trying to alert me to slow down and take breaks.

Although creepy, his appearance enticed me. His skin was rugged and toned, with a youthful glow that made me question his actual age. 40? 50? It was difficult to determine. He sported a three-piece tuxedo in the dead of summer, not just any summer, but a Floridian summer. I wondered how he didn't collapse from heatstroke. His slender build seemed similar to that of someone in the army or marines—built for durability and speed.

I knew I should be alarmed by him and I was, at first, but there was something so oddly comforting about him that I soon overcame my fear. He reminded me of someone I used to be close to, whose name I couldn't recall.

Days later, I woke up from an afternoon nap to see him sitting again in the same chair across from my bed. My senses seemed off, and I couldn't form the words to ask why he had reappeared. Almost as if reading my mind, he asserted his dominance by standing up. I panicked and tried to speak, but all I could manage to say was, "WHY?"

Chuckling at my uneasiness, he sat back down, crossing his legs. A soft smile remained on his face, but he leaned forward as if to talk. I leaned in, too, hoping he would say his name. Despite my enthusiasm, however, he merely leaned back in the chair and laughed softly. How was I supposed to know this man?

Frustrated by his lack of communication, I asked him again in a louder tone, "WHYYYY?!", and he realized I was not going to stop yelling until he revealed his identity. He stood up and approached the foot of my bed. Sitting down with a thud, he placed his right hand on my left knee and smiled. I recoiled quickly away from his touch, and he signaled to me to keep quiet. He had no right to touch me. He had gone too far, and the sense of comfort I once felt left immediately.

My brain could not come up with an answer to his appearance. Words left my mind and I couldn't form even the simplest of sentences – the beginning of my descent into madness.

3

The summer before my freshman year, I was ecstatic to be attending a new school and to be making new friends. By the end of my freshman year, my hopes had been destroyed. I decided I had to put my happiness first. I accepted that it was wrong for me to raise my hand to answer questions and that it was okay for people to make fun of my appearance. Of course, hearing their taunts stung, but I knew that the bullying directed at me was the direct result of their anger at themselves. Through all of this, I realized how unhappy and depressed this lifestyle made me feel. I have always loved being at school, but for the first time in fifteen years, I regretted it when my alarm blared at 6:30 am. It meant another day I would have to spend eating alone in an empty classroom or the bathroom. Teen romance movies have high school all wrong. There isn't a big group of welcoming peers waiting for you in homeroom, and the hottest guy in school doesn't fall for the shy but loveable nerd. I expected my experience to be just like all of those movies, but I understand now that my expectations were dreadfully wrong.

I decided to tell my parents everything about my freshman experience, including the hate, loneliness, and isolation, and they agreed that things needed to change. Unbelievably, I convinced my parents to move to Florida, so I could go to an international school that focuses on athletics as well as academics. It seemed like a dream, and it was. Each morning I woke up feeling energized and excited for what the day might hold. Words cannot express the awesome experience I had at my new school. At 16 years old, I thought I had life by the balls. I formed a study group comprised of some of the funniest and most focused people I knew. I was doing so well in school that my counselors spoke to me about Ivy League colleges. I was also having a blast with my golf coach and teammates on the course. My life seemed perfect, and I was the epitome of happiness. I thought it would just keep getting better, and better, and better. However, my junior year marked the beginning of my two-year fight for survival.

4

By the end of my sophomore year, I knew I wanted to board on campus for my junior year. During the year, when my parents picked me up at 6:00 pm from school, my happiness dissipated, similar to a child who is forced to leave Disneyland. If I had made it this far with my persuasive skills, maybe I could convince my parents to allow me to board. Just because I lucked out the first time, though, I knew I could not take this lightly. To change my parents' minds from "no" to "absolutely" wouldn't be easy. Financially, it would be an added expense that my parents would have a hard time justifying, especially since they had already moved to Florida with me. My parents could barely afford the price tag for a day student, so how could I expect them to jump at the decision for me to stay on campus? I was in over my head, but as a Taurus, this did not halt me one bit.

I worked my tail off to receive an academic scholarship that would offset some of the additional costs of boarding. I thought if I could contribute financially, too, my parents would not be able to say no. I applied for several jobs and hoped they would not immediately place my resume in the trash because of my age and lack of work experience. Some of the posts I applied to were retail positions, and I hadn't figured out how they would work with my schedule. But if a company hired me, I would somehow find a way to work a few hours per week. I wasn't thinking clearly at this point, and it should have been obvious to me that something was wrong. Considering I had to be at school at 7:30 am for practice, and school let out at 6:00 pm, there was no feasible way of working an additional four to six hours when there are only twenty-four hours in the day. But still, I applied.

Weeks went by without any response to my many job applications. I already felt distraught by the growing illness blossoming inside of me, and this added to my discomfort. Convinced that I was going to be rejected by all of the employers and that it was only a matter of time before the rejection emails hit my inbox, I figured that boarding was not in the cards. It was quite a wild dream considering how my luck had been going up to that point, and I needed to be appreciative of what I had because I was truly fortunate. Then, suddenly, there was the email I had been looking for:

"Congratulations, Miss Kingsly."

My parents said that I was happier to learn of this news than when they told me we were moving to Florida. I *was* thrilled. Not only had a corporation hired me at the age of sixteen, but it was also my first-choice job—digital analyst for an ophthalmology magazine. I would calculate the views per post rate, analyze the reach audience of each column, and send interview requests to doctors for upcoming issues. The best part of it all was that this position allowed me flexibility. I would be able to work around my schedule because I'd work remotely from my laptop. Additionally, I would be immersed in medical culture, which would help me determine if medicine was a path I wanted to pursue in college.

On top of everything, I would be able to take care of my expenses, such as clothes and toiletries, which would allow me to appeal to my parents on the basis that they wouldn't have to contribute much to my lifestyle besides the additional boarding cost. I was shocked when they said *yes* and amazed by my power of persuasion. I had done it again!

5

I did not think anything could make me happier. The summer flew by until there were only two weeks before I would move into my new dorm. I spent the little free time I had left at the gym and the driving range. The Friday before moving in, I drove myself to the gym before my mom took me for last-minute dorm shopping. I stopped at a red light and scrolled through the feed of my Instagram. Everyone's life seemed to be vacuous, and I wanted to live for more. Finally, when the light turned green, I put my phone down and pressed the gas pedal, but the car did not move. Soon the harsh cacophony of horns from the cars lined up behind me rang through my ears and into my brain. I couldn't do anything as the sound swallowed me whole. My motor skills seemed to vanish. I tried once again to push the gas pedal, and this time, I successfully moved the car; unfortunately, I moved right into an intersection full of oncoming traffic. I saw the red Honda Civic hurtling towards me, but I only snapped out of it when I heard the screeching of its tires. I pushed the gas pedal as fast as I could and made a left into the gym's parking lot. Getting out, I saw the intersection across the street resume its normal traffic flow.

Everyone seemed all right, and there was no anger. I tried to reassure myself of this as I hyperventilated while walking across the gym parking lot. I was OK. Everyone was OK. Maybe listening to my gym playlist would ease my nerves. Slipping my earbuds in, I grooved to the catchy beat of one of my songs.

Nodding my head, I suddenly felt I needed to shake off what had happened with a run. Exercising, especially running, helped to clear my head. Standing on the treadmill, I slowly started increasing the speed by small increments until I hit my target speed. Left, right, left, right, left, right, left, right, left, right, right—*thud*! Suddenly, everything went dark.

6

When late September rolled around, I knew time was of the essence. I had not told my parents everything I was experiencing. It started with the man in my room but progressively worsened each week. I had a difficult time discerning my symptoms; how could I expect my parents to believe me? Also, I worried that if I admitted these things were happening to me, it would become my reality. I was terrified of being diagnosed as *sick*. Unable to face the truth that I was ill, I continued to lie to myself, which left me in a perpetual state of emotional numbness.

Each time I came home from school, I spent hours crying in my bathroom about how stupid I was to want to board. I had set myself up to fail, and I had wasted tons of my parents' hard-earned money. I began to believe I was a terrible person. But I couldn't control the sickness, could I? Would I be this sick if I didn't board? Maybe it was my fault, and I had to live with it. Whatever it was, I knew I could not live with it alone for much longer. I had to put aside the burden of guilt and face reality. Or did I?

I could blame the hallucinations—seeing Him—on a lack of sleep. Fainting on the golf course could be attributed to dehydration and heatstroke. The arthritic joint pain throughout my entire body could be due to engaging in an intense workout. Stumbling in the halls due to waves of dizziness could be blamed on consuming too much sugar. Stress and exhaustion may have been causing me to confuse the order and spelling of words in a sentence each time I read a textbook. The paranoia and anxiety that caused me to scream when someone tapped me on the shoulder could be justified due to the increasingly frightening violence in schools. Food sensitivities could be responsible for my vomiting an entire day's worth of food. Heart palpitations and a slow heart rate may have been caused by exerting myself too much. I could blame the severe intestinal cramps and bouts of vomit on overeating before exercising. But who could I blame when this was how I felt *every single day*?

Soon, it all began to make sense. Pieces of the puzzle fell into place as I retraced everything I did by rereading my daily journal. It made sense that my symptoms made no sense. I needed divine intervention; something similar to that red Honda civic barreling towards me. I needed something that would certify that something was wrong.

As the saying goes, *be careful what you wish for.* My moment of clarity soon came. It was a Friday, and I had collected all my dirty laundry, golf clubs, textbooks, and homework to go home for the weekend. My mom and I were scheduled to meet in the lobby of my dormitory around 6:45. My AP Biology class had a study session from 6:15 until 6:40 for the quiz on that upcoming Monday, giving me just enough time to sprint back to my dorm to grab my things. I texted my mom that I was running late, and she said she'd sign me out for the weekend while I finished packing my bags. Hiding my emotions at school had begun to be second nature for me, but as I walked out of my dorm with my mom, I tried to keep my composure and remain as calm as possible as I felt my emotional shell starting to crack. Piece by piece, I felt the layers of insecurities and my facade fall as we approached our car. As my mom unlocked the door, a jolt of pain ran down my spine and spread throughout my vertebrae. I couldn't move or turn my head. Tears began to form in my eyes as I stood motionless, watching my mom load my bags into the car. This experience hadn't happened before, and I panicked. With the last of my things in, she went to the driver's side and entered the car. I remained stationary, hoping she would turn and see me. I gasped for air when He put his hands around my throat. My eyes expanded, and I felt that with any sudden movement they would burst. He continued to squeeze tighter and tighter each time I resisted. His force exacerbated my panic, and I tried to throw a punch. I wasn't expecting what happened next.

"Two can play this game, Lauren."

And with that, he punched me, and I fell backward, similar to a slow-motion scene in a movie. I collided, shrieking, with the concrete. When my mother saw me fall and heard me wail, she rushed to my side, her face covered in tears.

Why wasn't she punching him or calling the police?

He calmed down after my mom started to stroke my hair. My mom hugged me from the front while he held me in his grasp from behind. I tried to listen to my mom as she spoke through a gush of tears. I tried to explain that he was behind me. I tried to do something to ease her pain, but I couldn't.

He pulled my hair back behind my ear and placed his palm on my neck. Leaning down on the ground, he whispered in my ear with a sinister tone.

"Have you had enough yet, Lauren?"

I tried to respond, but I couldn't speak the words that formed in my mind. I stood there, paralyzed by his force. I wanted to scream; I wanted to yell.

He whispered again after a moment of suspenseful silence.

"Good. I didn't think so."

And with that, he released his force, and he was gone. I fell flat onto the concrete from my sitting position with my mother's arms still around me.

"LAUREN, HONEY; CAN YOU HEAR ME?" she screamed.

I could, but the weight of my tongue felt too heavy to push the words out of my mouth. I flashed my eyes in my mom's direction, hoping it would be enough for her to realize I was okay. The sound of her wailing rang throughout my ear canal; at that moment, I knew there was something wrong with me. To this day, I still can recall the horrifying shriek of her voice that evening.

7

I knew one day he might cause me great harm, and I wouldn't survive. I hadn't acknowledged this conscientiously, but now it became clear that I had to speak up or I may die. The man was a serious threat. He continually told me I was dying, and I believed a day would come where he would seriously harm me. Each interaction became more violent and aggressive than the next, but there had to be a reason. I had a choice to not head for doom. If I let my parents know the depth of my situation, maybe they could get me help to tame him; that is, if they didn't place me into an insane asylum first.

I promised myself that I would tell my parents the full story when my mom and I returned home. Because of the intensity of that moment, my mom had strapped me into a lying position in the back seat. I could see the edge of the sunset from my view, and it gave me time to release some tears without my mom knowing. She was too distraught about what had happened; she most likely wouldn't question my behavior. It gave me time to formulate what I wanted to say. I'd tell them about the anxiety, anger, paranoia, vomiting, and, of course, *him*. Then it hit me, and I'm not talking about the door banging against my skull when my mom unexpectedly stopped. My mom didn't react to him while his hands were around my throat; didn't she see him? Was it all just a product of my imagination? *No*, I thought. It couldn't be, because it had all felt too real. *He* felt real. He couldn't be just a by-product of my imagination, because he had choked me.

Then, against my better judgment, I decided not to tell my parents about him and what he was doing to me, out of fear that they would institutionalize me. I joke about it now, but it frightened me to think that I'd wake up one morning in a padded room, handcuffed to a hospital bed without a recognizable face in sight. I've seen Dateline and what happens to someone when they mention they "see things", and it's not pretty. I didn't want to turn into a monster, hyped-up on a cocktail of anti-psychotic drugs and narcotics. I knew I wasn't insane, even though it sure felt like I was when He came around. I just had to prove this to my parents, which was becoming increasingly difficult to do.

8

When my mom and I pulled into the garage of our condominium, she approached our parking space hesitantly and stopped the car abruptly. Shifting the gear into park, she turned her makeup-splattered, tear-drenched face towards me.

"Honey, tell me the truth. What the hell is going on with you? You've been acting strange ever since move-in day, and I have no idea what the hell is wrong with you, but it's disconcerting to me. Today's events have put the icing on the cake, and I believe we should see someone. This afternoon wasn't normal, Lauren, you were paralyzed!"

She made some valid points, but I just couldn't tell her, because if I did, I soon would lose the only identity I had of myself. I couldn't take honors and AP classes if I spent my days as a rat in a hospital bed. High school was my only source of joy and my biggest distraction from my life. Without it, I would fall into a never-ending spiral of self-misery, wondering every single day if my illness was because of my own doing. It seemed worse than what I was going through at the time. However, I knew on a subconscious level that wouldn't be the case; my parents would be willing to work with me to accommodate the doctors' appointments and homework. The real reason I didn't tell her or my dad is because, looking back, I knew that this journey would be a long one; one that I was not yet capable of handling. But when is anyone really, ready? No one —let alone a teenage girl —ever expects to be this sick. I can say with certainty that my subconscious was right. But not even my subconscious knew the illness would rob me of two of my teenage years, which I can never regain.

9

Upstairs, my dad greeted me with one of his "world-famous" hugs—*bear hugs*, as I so lovingly named them when I was five years old. I remember how the name came about. One day in early summer, when we lived in New Jersey, I climbed to the top of my favorite tree in our backyard. It wasn't a very tall tree, but it had been a goal of mine for the longest time to climb to the top. I talked about it with my dad every day after he picked me up from school. Each day he would go with me outside and stand watching as I tried to conquer the challenge, determined to reach a little farther each day. It took me three months to accomplish this goal. I would go outside and try again until eventually one day I made it to the top. Joy and pride erupted from my tiny frame as I sat upon the top branch, looking down at my dad cheering and applauding me. I remember taking a mental photograph of my surroundings: the birds, the way the sunlight fell upon the trees around me, and my dad. I climbed down, and my dad opened his arms wide and wrapped them around me.

"L, I am so proud of you. See? I told you; little by little, as long as you keep trying, you will achieve it. This is true for any goal in life. Please remember that, sweetheart."

"Thanks, daddy! I felt like a bear crawling up the tree."

"Well, here is a hug for my little bear."

That's how the name Bear Hug was born. His hugs always made me feel better, regardless of what was occurring in my life.

It felt like being enveloped by a plush blanket: soothing, relaxing, and calm. Being in his arms again, I remembered that memory fondly. For once in several weeks, I felt at ease and happy. *If only I could be as joyful now as I did at that moment,* I thought. Like anyone with a life well-lived, I had my memories to bring me happiness in my darkest moments. That is, until I didn't remember them.

After a few minutes of stroking my dog Charlie's fur on the couch, I went into my room and crashed onto my bed. Lying there did ease the discomfort inside of me, but it did not comfort the mistake or pain I contended with each day. My life represented the movie Groundhog, where Bill Murray wakes up each day having to repeat the same activities over and over, which drives him nearly to death, but he wakes up again in the morning to repeat the same cycle. In my case, however, I woke up each day with flu-like symptoms: headache, chills, fever, nausea, vomiting, diarrhea, and dizziness, to name a few. Like Bill Murray, I felt insane, waking up feeling as crappy as I did the day before and repeating the same protocol of over-the-counter medications to make it through the day (hopefully). Lying there on my bed staring at the fan on my ceiling, I knew the time had come to say something, but I didn't know how. It wouldn't be long before I couldn't handle this on my own and my parents starting to grow increasingly concerned with my eating habits. It wouldn't be long before I imploded.

When my mom called me out for dinner, my stomach grew uneasy as I walked out of my room to the dining room table. It was incredibly unfortunate, because my Dad had been preparing my favorite meal; pasta Bolognese. Due to all of my dietary restrictions (I am allergic to dairy, soy, peanuts, and hazelnuts, and I also have a gluten intolerance), my pasta Bolognese lacked the essential ingredients most people believe make a pasta dish:

cheese and wheat. Some may disagree, but I noticed no difference in the quinoa pasta my dad used. It tasted divine to me.

Tonight, however, it sounded horrible—like vomit on a platter. My stomach couldn't handle anything else in its acidic pit, even though I had only eaten a few bananas and an almond butter and jelly sandwich the entire day. That in itself is alarming to most.

I picked and stirred the pasta around in the bowl to make it look as if I were eating. I stopped and gulped some water before returning to my stirring, my parents' voices inaudible as my focus was diverted to my dinner. It wasn't long, however, before I got their attention. Soon after I started to stir the pasta, *his* face appeared, along with my body, in a seemingly ordinary pasta bowl. With each pass I would take around the bowl, he would grab the tip of my fork and jab it into my stomach, ankle, knee, and head. I screamed in terror, yet no sound came from my mouth. He was delighted by my response. This experience seemed like something that you'd only see in movies, but it was my reality, and it was happening to me.

I blinked, thinking I was just overtired, and then I heard his satanic tone as he began speaking to me.

"Speak now or forever hold your peace, Lauren."

Beads of sweat rolled down my face and under my arms as my mom got up and held me in my chair. My eyes didn't blink; they remained focused on my bowl in front of me. She kept me in her arms, her voice inaudible as she stroked my hair. I don't remember much about how the rest of the evening went, but I do remember my mom locking up my Dad's knife set. I didn't have to say I was insane. My parents already knew.

10

I woke up thirteen hours later feeling the way I believe a person with a hangover might feel: dizzy, exhausted, nauseous, and ashamed of what happened the night before. (I'm allergic to alcohol, but witnessing my parents' experience, I believe 'hangover' is a perfect description). There was one difference between what I was experiencing and a hangover; however, I had no idea where I was. Everything around me seemed foreign. Looking at photos on the wall, I saw myself with a myriad of people whose names I didn't know. The print over my bathroom doorway with a name inscribed in calligraphy was no help, either.

I rubbed my eyes to rid them of sleep, hopeful it would also jog my memory. It didn't - until I saw *him* standing in the corner of my room, leaning against my desk, holding a martini. He no longer surprised me, but the choice of a cocktail this early (or so I thought) was weird. Stirring the tiny, sword-shaped swizzle stick, he noticed I had risen and came to sit on the edge of my bed. I pulled up the blanket for more coverage. There was nothing more uncomfortable than being braless around a strange man early in the morning.

Rubbing his hands together, he seemed focused on how to tell me something. I sat there silently as he continued to fidget, with one eyebrow raised slightly higher than the other. He took deep breaths and then finally repositioned himself and looked me in the eyes.

We both sat back and paused. I started to think that maybe there was a reason he came around. Why did he suddenly appear whenever my symptoms worsened? There must be some correlation...

"Ok, why should I listen to you? You've done nothing but torment me, scare me, and psychologically damage me; what else do you want? A friendship? I don't see that ever happening with the way you treat me. How would interacting with you be beneficial for me in any way? Why should I ever listen to you? In fact, why am I even talking to you right now?"

His eyes never looked up into mine. He slumped in the chair and traced the outline of his lips with his finger. Never would I trust him. Never.

"Well, aren't you going to say something??"

He grabbed my hand and lifted his head. I could see tears; they traced the outline of his face and rolled down his cheek. With his fingers intertwined in mine, he sobbed. Was this even real, or was it some act? *Who knows at this point?* I thought.

He wiped off his face with his jacket sleeve, with his lips parted slightly.

"Because you are going to die soon if you don't get some help, my darling."

11

I don't remember my reaction after he murmured those words. I didn't recollect this event until I skimmed through my journal months later. What I do remember, though, is that the room went black – an occurrence I began to be oh so familiar with.

Later in the day I awoke to the sound of my dog, Charlie, barking. *I must have fallen back to sleep after he left*, I thought. At first, my brain couldn't distinguish between Charlie's barking and my dream. It was unfortunate, because it was blissful. I was sitting in my backyard in New Jersey underneath the oak tree at the top of the hill, overlooking our pool and Charlie. Sitting there, I felt at peace. I only felt this calm when I sat here, in this spot. It was my happy place. No matter where else I've been in the world, I always come back to that spot. Anytime I sat there, it would bring immense happiness and I longed to have those feelings again. It was refreshing to dream of something tranquil instead of one of the hellish nightmares I had been having of *him*.

In my dream, Charlie's barking became the sound of our neighbors' dogs playing with each other. I watched as two little, white fluff balls chased each other with fury across the expansive plane of their backyard. I remember wishing I could have a day on which I could feel as carefree as those dogs and enjoy simple things, such as an unusually colored leaf on the ground or an oddly long strand of grass. As the smile spread across my face, my brain finally distinguished the two sounds, and I opened my eyes. Charlie's barking wasn't his playful bark; this was his "there is danger" bark. Frantically, I ran to my door and tried to open it, but the handle was jammed. Like a mad woman, I kicked, screamed, and put all my strength into opening the door. Luckily, it opened. Running out into the living room, I couldn't believe the sight. *He* had Charlie by the collar, squeezing tightly and then releasing it, repeatedly. I could see the pain and helplessness in Charlie's eyes as they flashed in my direction.

"LET GO OF MY DOG, NOW!" I shouted.

He looked over, acknowledging my presence, and released Charlie. Then he walked over to me as Charlie ran frantically into my room. I ran to shut the door before he had the chance to enter my room. Jamming the door shut, he grabbed me by the hips and pinned me against the wall outside of my room. I thought I knew how to handle this, but I was defenseless. The only thing I could do to protect myself was to yell with the small amount of courage I had left.

"WHAT THE HELL DO YOU WANT FROM ME? WHAT? TELL ME! TELL ME, DAMN IT!"

Closing my eyes, I prepared for his brute force. *Please, please, don't hit me,* I thought. *PLEASE. I can't handle this.* Praying, I hoped that someone above would hear me and stop this madness. But nothing happened.

12

I sat solemnly at dinner that evening, picking at the grilled chicken and mixed vegetables my Dad prepared. I couldn't stop thinking about what he said. *Die? Am I going to die soon?* My parents were talking about a music festival taking place downtown the next day when I abruptly interrupted them.

"Um, I think I should see someone."

"Who do you want to see, L?" my Dad chimed.

"A psychologist. I need to vent a little bit."

My parents nodded in unison before my mom spoke.

"Sure, Lauren. Your father and I agree. We want you healthy and feeling happy again. Maybe it's just stress; however, if it's something more, you should get it off your chest. Always know we are here for you if you ever need to talk to us about something."

"Yeah, thanks, Mom. I know. I love you guys."

"We love you too," they both replied with a sigh of relief.

The next morning I woke up early to pack my belongings for my dorm. My brain, unable to comprehend why I was up at 4:30 am, couldn't even execute the simple task of putting matching socks together. Something was off. As the rising sun cast a shadow on my windowsill an hour later, my mind was still mush. At this point, this seemed elementary compared to my episodes with *him*, so I didn't stress too much about it, and I decided to start getting ready for the school day. Sifting through a sea of New York Times Op-Ed sections, clutter, and the occasional old homework assignment, I forged a path to my bathroom. I fluctuated between pigtails and a classic high ponytail, but I finally went with just a simple ponytail. Anything more elaborate seemed too complicated for my brain. After doing my hair, I finished my look with a dab of tinted sunscreen and a quick brush of mascara. I went back to my desk to grab my bag and, with that, I was out the door.

My mom stopped me before I could leave the condo.

"Whoa, Lauren. Who did your makeup this morning? A clown? Ha. I'm not letting you go to school until you wash your face."

Ouch, harsh! I mean, by no accounts would I consider myself very savvy with makeup application, but still… I walked back to my bathroom and glanced in the mirror. I looked fine. My makeup didn't appear smeared, smudged, or in the wrong places. Still, I washed my face to please my mom and ran out the door. Afterward, I pretended to be using the bathroom, but I grabbed my pink sneakers and switched out of my flip-flops. I just needed a few more minutes to myself before I had to brace for another week. I just needed to come to clarity about my reality. I just wanted this to be over. I didn't know who I was or who I was becoming, and I didn't like this person. Thoughts percolated and floated through my mind as I spent an enormously long time trying to tie my shoes. *Up, under, around, and out, then knot? No, no, no; bunny ears? Wait…knot, tie, loop and another loop—wait…loop and tie; no, scratch that…loop and knot and tie and bow.*

13

In the blink of an eye, the school day ended. Thank goodness. My day consisted of staring at the word *the* repeatedly, because each time I read it, its spelling altered (like the visuals at a funhouse, minus the fun) and doubting my knowledge in AP Biology when I knew I could handle the course load. (I loved Biology when I knew how to spell!). Then a nervous breakdown occurred in the second-floor bathroom while vomiting while simultaneously wondering whether my life plan was a stupid one (because what teenage girl *doesn't* have a nervous breakdown?). I hoped that when I returned to my precalculus class, no one would remember the awkwardly long time I had been away (I doubted they would, though, considering most of them spent their time passing notes and gas). The grand finale of the day came when I realized I had another AP Biology quiz on Friday and would have to break out the phonics cards again. (Yeah, you read that right; 16 and using phonics cards #normal.) Shockingly, the cards had worked; on my previous quiz, I received a grade of 87%, so I had high hopes that my score would be similar to the next one. The cards were my little secret, though.

I strolled through the campus center, walking past the game room and into the jungle of the cafeteria. Walking through the sliding glass doors, I noticed every person in the room staring at me. I looked down at myself, wondering if my shirt was on backwards or if I was wearing my lunch. I saw nothing wrong. I hoped that when I turned around, everyone would move on to something or someone else, as most teenagers' attention spans are approximately five seconds long. Nope. It worsened. As I walked down the aisle of tables, all eyes were upon me, and as I looked to my left and right, the students' eyes followed me. The big-screen TV started to glitch, and he appeared on the monitor. What?! How is he on the news broadcast? This broadcast was live from Tampa! Who allowed him to shut down the local news broadcast? I gulped, and sweat began to build upon parts of my body I didn't know could sweat. *Please don't talk to me*, I thought. *Not in front of all of these people.*

He appeared when he could make me the most uncomfortable. I hate being the center of attention, and right then and there I was standing, awkwardly, in front of hundreds of teenagers.

His eyes enticed me. Of course, they were on a large monitor, so naturally they would draw me in, but still; his eyes seemed like a vortex pulling me with a greater force with each step I took. His intensity frightened me. Eventually, I knew I would cave in to his desires. Perhaps he was right; maybe I was dying. But why should I listen to a man who tries to torment and kill me?

"Hello, Lauren."

His diabolical tone sent chills down my spine. Everyone's eyes widened in anticipation of my response.

"I can't take this anymore. Why should I trust you, out of anyone else in the world?"

He nodded in approval. I guess he knew his behavior was unacceptable. Or maybe he was planning something more diabolical.

"Well, then, I guess it's settled; your Mom and Dad are next on my list."

Panicking, I gave in. "NO, don't you dare. Fine, I'm yours. Do what you want. I don't care. I'm your prisoner. I'll listen. Just don't go after my parents. They don't deserve this."

"Good. I knew you would obey me. Everyone, you don't have to keep staring at Lauren. Mission accomplished."

With that, the TV reverted to its regular broadcast. Everyone went back to their lives and conversations, while I remained in the nightmare that was my life.

Ironically, he wasn't the scariest part. After a few weeks, I became accustomed to having an unnamed man accompany me throughout the day and sit next to me in class, chatting away about gas prices or his preference at Starbucks, while trying to focus on my teacher, who was giving a presentation about the Krebs cycle. The scariest part was knowing that an illness was maturing inside of me, over which I had no control. A sense of helplessness marred my self-confidence, as I thought it was my fault. Those feelings intensified as days turned into weeks. I went from not knowing how to tie my shoes to not being able to recognize friendly faces in the hall. I went from knowing how to describe what was bothering me to not knowing how to articulate a sentence. Keeping my cover proved harder and harder as the weeks passed. How could I maintain my sense of being as my foundational core cracked deeper and deeper each day?

14

The next morning I called my coach to tell him I had a terrible migraine and wouldn't be able to come to practice. I didn't have a "migraine"; I needed to be alone. All things considered, it wasn't that much of a lie, because my life was an ongoing migraine from one day to the next. My give-a-crap meter read at an all-time low.

Lack of sleep also contributed to my decision to miss practice. I was preoccupied with how to explain to my parents the depths of my misery. I didn't care if my parents thought I was insane; I couldn't do this alone anymore. The excuses for my maniacal behavior had to stop. I needed to sit down and tell them everything, from start to finish. If they truly loved me, they would understand and help. But what bothered me was why I was so afraid to tell them. It's not like I robbed a bank or stole someone's identity. The fact that I had so much resistance to telling my mom and dad the truth scared me; so much so that I chickened out and waited another two weeks before I told them. But for now, I concluded that the fear stemmed from my subconscious. If I told them, my pain would no longer be imaginary or my own doing. It would be real, and I didn't want to face reality - yet.

Later that afternoon, my parents picked me up before my free period to go to my first appointment with the psychologist. Indian summer had kicked in, and the unrelenting heat muted my entire family for the duration of the ride. In retrospect, the high temperature probably wasn't the only reason for our discomfort.

Once we arrived at the psychologist's office, I noticed the soft hum of gospel music that played on her boom box. My dad joked about how he hadn't seen one of that caliber since he was in college, and that seemed to break the tension between the three of us.

Was what I experienced daily, including visions of him, just a manifestation of God? Was God angry at me for not talking to him anymore? Did neglecting my religion and roots cause hallucinations and chronic pain? At this point, I considered anything as a possible root cause. I craved an answer—any answer. As unreasonable as it sounds, I decided to start to pray each night, hoping that some divine intervention would occur and cure me of all my ailments.

Within a few minutes of our arrival, Dr. T emerged from her office. She motioned for us to come back to her office, which contained a nylon couch, a bookshelf containing several "self-diagnosis" books, and inspirational sayings on each of the four walls: "Dream On," "Nothing is Impossible," and "Follow Your Heart," to name a few. The second statement, "Nothing is Impossible," was patently wrong, because I tried relentlessly to get rid of *him*, but he was still around.

Nothing about the appointment was comfortable, primarily because my mom and dad sandwiched me in on either side of the couch. My claustrophobia, made worse by my confinement, made the first fifteen minutes of the appointment unbearable.

My mom started off the session by explaining to Dr. T why I wanted to come here. She related my strange behavior, gave a history of my personality, and spoke about her and my dad's concerns. Dr. T sat cross-legged in her chair across from us, taking vigorous notes. She nodded her head every few sentences to assure my mom she was still listening. Afterward, my dad inserted a few points he thought my mom had missed. With that, Dr. T told my parents to leave, and my claustrophobic self was relieved. As the door closed, I lay down on the couch with my head facing her.

"I know you aren't insane, Lauren, and I don't believe this is a psychological issue. Just know that anything you say is safe here. I'm all ears."

A flood of relief came over me. She said I am not insane. *I am not crazy.* To reassure myself, I whispered the sentence to myself several times before I thought to respond.

"It is hard for me to rationalize that I am not psychotic when every day I have this crippling anxiety that causes walls to move."

"Which walls move, Lauren?"

"My dorm room walls. Sometimes when I open the door to my dorm after a long day, my walls move closer together. My 8x10 room suddenly feels like a long corridor."

"Have you ever considered the walls moving to be a cry for help from your subconscious? In other words, do you feel lost, Lauren?

"Absolutely."

"Why do you feel lost?"

"I am a straight-A student. I was on the road to becoming a collegiate golfer, and suddenly this school year, I can't read the word *the* because each time I see it, the order of the letters changes. I can't eat because it causes severe intestinal pain, and

I can't sleep because of my nerves. I can't do anything because of *him*."

Oh no. I can't tell my therapist about him.

"Who is he? A boyfriend?"

"No, no, no," I said, trying to backtrack.

"Sorry; my brain is a little disoriented. I've noticed this happening recently. I meant to say *this*. I can't do anything because of this."

"Oh, ok, sure."

She knew she hit a nerve but, thankfully, she didn't interrogate more. Phew. Crisis averted. I came prepared to let go of the emotions and sickness I had been facing, but I wasn't willing to speak about him.

The session went quickly, and within half an hour, we used up all the time.

"Lauren, I think what's going on is that you are experiencing situational anxiety and depression. Junior year of high school is a difficult time, and with your hopes of going to an Ivy League or similar institution, you are putting a great deal of stress on yourself. The one thing I will say is that, since your dad does have ulcerative colitis and you are experiencing irritable bowel symptoms, I would suggest going to see a gastroenterologist. Let's aim for a session each week and, hopefully, you should be back on track by January. Do you have any questions for me, Lauren?"

"Nope; I'm good. Thank you for your time." I responded.

"Of course. See you next week, same time."

And with that, I stood up, waved goodbye, and left her office. I walked down the long corridor to see my parents, who were whispering about how they thought my session went. My mom held her thumb clenched between her other four fingers. She only did this when she was extremely nervous, which, for her, happened once in a blue moon. I told them it went well and that I felt better. Lies. I said that my psychiatrist believed stress was the culprit, due to my changing environment and my plans for the future. I told them I trusted her explanation and that I should be fine by January with the help of her sessions. 'Lies upon lies, upon sweet little lies.' (Fleetwood Mac makes up 52% of my playlist).

Seeing how distraught my parents were over a simple appointment made me second-guess whether I should tell them the full truth. Would they be able to handle it? Maybe they wouldn't understand or care. As I got into the back of my dad's SUV, I decided again not to tell them; at least not until I had a few more sessions with Dr. T. I would probably be in a better frame of mind by then.

Driving along I-75, a feeling of panic came upon me when I saw the sea of brake lights ahead. We had grown relatively accustomed to the quirky traffic patterns of Florida (rush-hour levels of traffic at 11:30 am, for example). But seeing the abrupt halt just a few hundred yards away from our car concerned me because we were traveling well over 70 mph, and it was only 4:07 pm. Rush hour traffic usually doesn't begin until at least five. I thought there must have been an accident.

As my dad slammed on the brakes to stop us from ending up in the trunk of the silver Lexus in front of us, *he* appeared. He hijacked our car, and suddenly our brakes became useless.

"NO. Don't you dare! DON'T YOU DARE!!" I screamed, trying to push him off my dad's lap.

I punched forcefully as I continued to scream. My tantrum was interrupted as he turned and faced me.

"Pinky promise you won't ever bring up my name again and I'll go away…for now."

"I PINKY PROMISE," I yelled, trying to catch my breath. An accident seemed inevitable at our current speed.

"All right, wonderful. Bye."

15

As the weeks passed, it suddenly became more comfortable to keep my composure. I attributed this to my sessions with Dr. T. Having an hour each week to vent about any topic under the sun helped alleviate stress. It did nothing for my physical symptoms, but it still helped. The paranoia and anxiety were still at an all-time high, as evidenced by these text messages I sent to a friend:

Me, 10:26 pm: "Hey, can we talk? I feel like I am drowning. When I'm in certain social situations, and I realize I don't fit in and consciously I don't mind, but subconsciously it gets to me and then I realize what if I never do? What if I am that person that lives alone for eternity and eats cat food??"

Me, 10:31 pm: "And then I can go off on this tangent that maybe I am like this because I am supposed to be some great leader that must go through adversity, but it's complicated. I don't know if I can be a leader. I don't know. People stare at me in the halls and think I am some weird creature who morphed into a human. I can't relate to anyone, no one If I start to speak, they look at me as if I am speaking Dutch.

Me, 10:34 pm; "All the girls on my floor especially."

Me, 11:38 pm: "I'll see you tomorrow. Thanks for listening and being there. Goodnight."

Besides my horrible grammar and vocabulary choices, my illness is evident in these texts. No normal human feels this self-conscious. No healthy human being stays up until 2:37 am wondering if their AP Biology teacher hates them because they used their first name to address them by accident. I wasn't normal, but it wasn't my fault. Responsibility on the other hand, leaned toward me.

Telling myself I was ok each day only made the disease intensify. I never thought a 17-year-old could have a mid-life crisis, let alone a breaking point. Well, they can, and it isn't pretty when that happens. Trust me, I know. I reached it.

16

As my eyelids fluttered open the following morning, I rolled over to look at my phone on my charger. 4:36 am. Usually, I wake up at 4:30 to study for an AP Bio quiz, but as far as I could remember, I didn't have one that week. Or did I? My brain hadn't booted up yet, and everything seemed fuzzy, especially the intense pain radiating from my stomach.

I rubbed the sleep from my eyes, allowing my eyes to adjust to the light. But not even the clearest of eyes could have understood what I saw in front of me.

It looked like bacteria and a mix of intestines. As the layers of epithelial tissue dissolved, the image of my stomach became clearer. My stomach churned, and my roasted turkey and pasta dinner from the night before halted as the bacteria ate through my stomach lining. The sight was horrid, and the acid smelled awful. I have never been so fascinated and terrified at the same time. The food needed an exit, and since my stomach was no longer a route, the food made its way—rather quickly, I might add—up to my esophagus.

No, no, I thought. *I hate vomiting; it terrifies me. Breathe. This isn't happening, THIS ISN'T HAPPENING.* My fear of vomiting only furthered the process, and suddenly, I felt the chunks of food brush up against my teeth.

Sweat exited from every crevice of my body. My sheets were visibly wet; not just from sweat but from the acid. I wanted to get up, but being on the top bunk made the trip to the bathroom below even more daunting.

Screw it, I thought. I jumped from my top bunk rather ungracefully to the floor below and ran to the bathroom as food and other particles escaped my mouth. Between bouts of vomiting and screaming from the burning sensation of my stomach acid, I could hear the cacophony of my phone buzzing. *Crap!! I forgot to text Jay. I am going to have a suspension now. Great. I don't think flesh-eating bacteria is a great excuse, but I'll have to try it.* Making the situation worse, I could hear the faintest sound of my mom's ringtone—Stewie Griffin saying "Mom" repeatedly. She must have heard from Jay that I am not at practice, and she's worried. Thoughts circulated throughout my mind as I tried to concentrate in between episodes of vomiting. There was nothing I could do. I was helpless. *WHAT AM I SUPPOSED TO DO?* I muttered to myself, with tears cascading down my face.

"You should go to the hospital and stop telling yourself you're ok. Because you're not."

I could recognize that voice from a mile away. Looking down at the murky brown water of the toilet bowl, I was afraid to look up to see him. There wasn't much to be angry about with him since he had taken me prisoner, but I still felt enraged, as any ordinary person would.

I wiped my eyes with a slip of toilet paper and turned to face him. He seemed unalarmed and bored with my "performance."

"Look. Grab my phone from my bed and I will call my mom and tell her to take me to the hospital, okay? Is that what you want?" I asked, as my tears came faster.

"Fine. Go to the hospital; get a random prescription that will help with absolutely nothing. But if you even mention seeing me or talking to me, this morning's episode will seem like a walk in the park compared to the fury and hell that await you."

He paced over to my bunk bed with heavy footsteps. Weirdly, I felt comforted by him. I could count on him to keep my secrets just as I held his; he was the one constant variable in my life. Even though he was a sickening creature, I found solace in his wrath. At least I had someone who cared to tell me I was sick.

"Here's your damned phone." He tossed the phone, hitting me on my left temple.

17 Unread Messages from Coach Jay, Mom, and Dad

Great. I'm screwed.

As my unsteady voice grew stronger, I asked Siri to call my Mom.

Calling Mom.

She picked up immediately. "Honey, what the hell?! Jay texted me saying you're MIA and your father and I have been worried sick. Are you ok? Where are you? You can't just ignore us like this. Tell me you're okay. Please!"

I suddenly became unhinged, and I unleashed my anger at her.

"MOM, I AM SICK. I HAVE BEEN UP SINCE 4:36 AM VOMITING AND DIZZY AND FEELING AWFUL. MY STOMACH LINING IS VISIBLE, AND BLOOD IS EVERYWHERE. I NEED TO GO TO THE HOSPITAL. I CAN SEE MY INTESTINES. THE WALLS ARE CLOSING IN ON ME, AND IT'S FORCING FOOD TO COME OUT OF ME LIKE NIAGARA FALLS. I CAN'T HANDLE THIS ANYMORE. I NEED HELP. NOW. But please don't be mad at me."

The silence on the phone line between us was deafening. My manic mind told me *she hates me and thinks that I am a dramatic brat. She's going to tell me I am watching too much TV and that I need to be realistic because I can't see my intestines. But I could; clear as day. She probably thinks I am having an anxiety attack. She is going to ground me. She going to say I am stressed out and that I need more sleep. She might be thinking that I reached my breaking point.* If she did, she was right.

Suddenly, I heard tears on the other end of the phone.

"Lauren, I am coming to get you. Stay where you are, ok? Everything is going to be all right. I'll be there in 20 minutes, and we can go to the hospital, ok? Just don't leave your room. Try to lie down or do something that makes you comfortable. It is going to be ok. It is going to be ok."

I believe she said it twice to reaffirm herself more than me. Regardless, I felt better knowing she would be with me soon. She would help, but we would both quickly realize that everything was *not* going to be okay.

17

We made our way downstairs to the lobby of my dormitory. It was a Friday and kids could be seen relaxing on the couches and beanbags surrounding the TV. Sounds of gunfire startled me as I stood watching the football game between USC and the University of Washington. I soon realized the sound came from the Xbox connected to the other TV, but it still didn't help my unsettled nerves. I felt akin to a cat in heat; anything spooked me. Spooked as I was, the reassurance of getting to the bottom of my health problems helped. My mom signed me out of campus at the campus life desk, but she still stood at the desk. I assumed she was signing me out for the week. *Score!* Inwardly, I gave a similar exclamation to the one elicited by the touchdown USC had just scored. I looked over to see my mom and my houseparent, Mary, chatting. Mary's facial expression showed signs of dismay and despair. Mary was very friendly; we had a good rapport, and I bet she was upset by what my mom had shared with her. *It's okay*, I thought. I had trouble, too, believing my reality.

Soon my mom motioned for me to come over, and we walked out of the dorm into the courtyard. The total distance from the dorm to the parking lot is about half a mile, but it seemed longer at the pace we walked. Since I had broken down on the phone three hours earlier, I felt emotionally vulnerable enough to speak more about what I was going through. I told her about how I couldn't eat, the paranoia and anxiety, about how I had to buy phonics flashcards to relearn how to spell words, and that I woke up in puddles of sweat from nightmares. I told her about how it felt as if the walls of my dorm were closing in on me. I spoke about the vomiting and the dizziness I experienced with each step I took. I told her everything except about *him*.

Her composure cracked, and I hated to see my mom cry, but I knew I had to spill it. Maybe it was easier for her not to know, but I felt invested, and didn't hold back. We were just a few steps from the car when she broke into hysterics.

"Hon, how come you didn't tell me? I don't want you to suffer alone! How were you able to manage this past month? And don't take this the wrong way, but how are your grades still all As? How much time does it take you at night to study? Kids aren't looking at you. You aren't weird; you are wonderful, Lauren. Oh, my little girl, I am so sorry I didn't know. I am so sorry."

As she wrapped me in her arms, I began to cry, too. I had my lifeline here the entire time, and I refused to use it.

18

We decided to go to the children's hospital in St. Petersburg. We chose it because, based on google reviews of other hospitals in the area, this hospital seemed the most promising. We put the address in the navigation system in my mom's car, and we were off. It was 36 miles away. In approximately 47 minutes, I would finally find out the cause of my hellish reality.

I pushed the seat back down so I could lie down in a more comfortable position. It was 12:30 pm and rush hour would soon begin. The drive would be a long one. The first segment of our trip was silent for a good reason. We both needed to come down off our euphoric high of being able to speak meaningfully again and realize what lay ahead. Of course, I didn't want to focus on that; I wanted to enjoy the time for what it was before we learned the depth of the journey. The calm before the storm.

I watched the waves of the bay as we neared the Skyway Bridge. Only in Florida could you be a few feet away from the ocean and driving in a car - pure awesomeness. When we first moved here, it frightened me to be so close to the brute force of mother nature, but now I appreciated the beauty and how unique it was to be able to say I drove by the ocean. Not many people could say that. Although inspiring, it did prove to be a bit of a nightmare during hurricane season. The bridge and highway became useless because of the flooding, making commuting a bear for those not living in the bay area. The highway is safe, but it could easily cross a line and become deadly. In life, too, there is a fine line to cross between life and death. Why did everything I think about suddenly turn into something so metaphorical? Hmm…

"Hey, Lauren; can you remember the very first symptom? Did you wake up one day and suddenly feel differently, or was it a slower progression of symptoms that brought you to this?"

Snap back to reality, Lauren!

"Hmm…well, truthfully, I just remember being at the gym one morning about a week before move-in and it started there."

"What happened, Hon?"

"I was taking a break from the spin bike before I went in to use the bench press, and I felt rather faint. I had been off the bike for about fifteen minutes or so, consumed by some college article I found on College Confidential. My heart rate accelerated quickly, and I began to overheat. I felt as if I couldn't get enough air, and my breathing became delayed. And then, *boom*. The room went dark."

"Lauren, how come you never told me? That must have been incredibly frightening."

"Well, I didn't think much about it, Mom. I just assumed it had to do with dehydration and a deficiency of electrolytes."

"Did you drink more the following time you went to the gym?"

"Yes."

"Did it help?"

"No."

"Do you think that Dr. T is right? Do you sincerely believe that this is all from the stress you've put on yourself?"

"No, I mean, look. Throughout my life, I've tended to stress out more than necessary, and it wreaks havoc on my body in certain ways. Exhaustion was common, but I've never had any of these other symptoms. But anything is possible. Stress can do unimaginable things to a person's body. I once read that high levels of cortisol can lead to several cancers and affect different areas of the brain. Scientists are now looking to see if chronic stress can—"

"Lauren, stop making excuses. Yes; you are the type to stress, but it has never produced the symptoms you're having. A few, yes, but not all of them. Not all of these symptoms are stress-induced, but the stress certainly doesn't ease it. There is something else going on."

There is something else going on.' These words reverberated like an echo inside my head. I didn't want to accept the mystery of the unknown; my scientific and analytical mind had to have an answer, and I assumed I would receive it by the end of the day, which calmed me for the remainder of the car ride.

Pulling into a parking space, my mom and I held hands as we both took a deep breath. We had to remain calm and hopeful. We promised each other that whatever the diagnosis, we would be okay and get through it as a family. I'm pretty sure my mom thought I had a terminal illness at that moment. Knowing how frail my health had been, impending doom seemed like a logical place for her imagination to travel.

Inside, my mom admitted me. We then waited to see the physician on-call. We waited. And waited. And waited. The long wait allowed my mind to wander and, for the first time, I questioned why I hadn't seen *him*. It had been a while, and I figured that he would start to appear more regularly (I told myself this to calm down when he did present himself at random). Maybe he would be gone, since I was getting help, and I would have an answer soon. *Well, the day was still young. There is plenty of time for him to show up again*, I thought. Oddly, I missed him.

Consumed in thought, I couldn't even hear when the nurse called my name.

"Lauren, hon, we're up."

"Huh? Wha-? Oh, yes, coming. Sorry."

The moment had arrived. I would know my illness, and I could continue with my life. I had never been so excited to hear bad news in my life. How ironic. Once my blood pressure, temperature, and pulse were taken, the nurse told us to follow her to my room. I then changed into a gown and lay down on the bed, staring at the door like a dog who misses its owner. My mom and I didn't speak until the doctor came in.

My mom shared every detail of my pain and suffering, and I occasionally interjected with anything she missed. Well, again, except for *him*. Within the first few minutes, I could see this doctor had no clue as to what was wrong with me. Her facial expression gave her away as she tried to comprehend the daunting list of symptoms I experienced. She pretended to jot down notes and then went through her checklist of procedures. CAT Scan, MRI, X-ray, and CBC, along with a few others that I missed as I dozed off. We started with the X-ray, the least harmful of procedures, to get a quick overview. I had a feeling nothing would show up. My intuition led me to believe so.

About twenty minutes later, the doctor came in with an odd grin. That's never a good sign. Did I have malignant tumors spreading throughout my body? A rare liver disease? Only one ovary instead of two? I came to learn through my medical history that when doctors smile, it means you are a very sick patient or an "exciting" case.

She proceeded to show us on the X-ray that the discomfort I had been feeling was due to gas. Wait, gas? Gas was causing me to frequently vomit due to stabbing pains throughout my lower abdomen and leaving me unable to eat anything solid for days? That sounded completely irrational, even for me, incredible really, considering my mental state.

My mom wasn't convinced, either; she scratched her head in disbelief. We both looked at each other with confusion as the doctor continued to ramble on about how gas pains can present themselves in various ways.

I wanted someone to understand my pain like *he* did. It seemed that no one was capable of listening, because they either didn't care or didn't choose to. My mom and dad cared, but it was hard for me to put into words what was going on. I had grown accustomed to the idea of having to live with the jarring pain I woke up with daily, and it was hard to distinguish it from my other symptoms. How could I explain to someone that every time I sat up, it felt as if someone had stabbed me in my spine, or that each time I read a book the order of the words would shift, making it seem like garbled rambling, or that when I took notes for school, I couldn't write on the left side of the page because my eyes could only see the right? There was too much to say and too little time to explain it. Doctors are human, and complex cases are too daunting and time-consuming to diagnose. Therefore, it seemed logical to treat one single symptom to bring me some relief. That is, until the following week when I would reappear again with another complaint. Is this fair and the best treatment for me, the patient? Hell no.

Her voice continued to echo in my head as I thought about her diagnosis. She proceeded to tell me that she was going to give me a prescription for a high dose of Gas-X when I interrupted her.

"What if I told you that, in the last week, I spent every morning vomiting every bit of solid food I'd had? Or that each time I try to take a bite of solid food, my mouth regurgitates it? Or that I get dizzy just by standing up too quickly? Or that everyone who speaks to me seems as if they are mumbling? Or that I stay up at night crying because the walls of my dorm room appear to move closer together, inch by inch, until the two walls are only a body's width apart and I can't move a single muscle? Would you still think all of this was caused by gas pains?"

"Well no, — I…"

"Then why do you confidently stand there telling my mom and me, after everything my mom has told you, that the pain I have been experiencing is due to gas? If you know it isn't, why are you lying to us? Is that what they teach doctors nowadays; to lie to their patients when they don't feel like investigating the whole story? Hmm? Why won't you listen to me? Take a step back from your scripted routine of shoving prescription pills down patients' throats and listen, dammit."

My mom, clearly rattled by the situation, raised her voice after my last sentence. "Lauren, that's enough."

"No, it's not, Mom. This doctor is confidently standing here telling me all my problems will go away if I fart, when both you and I know that isn't the case. I need someone to help me. I need help, okay? Why won't she help me? Hello? Woman? I NEED SERIOUS MEDICAL ATTENTION, AND YOU DON'T SEEM TO CARE, DO YOU? WHAT IN THE HELL IS WRONG WITH YOU? I NEED MORE THAN THIS;

CAN'T YOU SEE? GET ME AN ACTUAL DOCTOR. SHOW ME THE TRUTH."

He came in suddenly and swiftly and jumped on top of me. As my lungs gave out, my eyes grew heavy and closed. He held my mouth shut with his smooth fingers. Pushing me back against the bed, he whispered in my ear: "Good girl, Lauren, good girl."

I woke up next to *him*, but with fur cuffs around my arms and strapped to the hospital bed. Delusions crowded my mind. Looking down at my wrist, I noticed a bracelet with the word "MENTAL" on it. Great. They think I am insane, too. Reality and my hallucinations were intertwined.

19

This marked the first of several trips to the hospital. Each visit being more daunting than the last. I was a typical 'newbie patient': delusional and optimistic, assuming the building would bestow upon me a 'miracle', performed by a doctor who would fix my ailments with the prescription of a magic pill or treatment. This common false expectation creates a climate of phobia of hospitals. I understand. I had it myself. My visits were frequent, and I observed a hospital routine or protocol that repeated itself regardless of which hospital I went to. Treat a single symptom, throw medication at it, and move to the next patient. Our health care system is failing hundreds of thousands of people, treating a symptom, and not fixing the source.

I have devised a list of rules (more like commandments) that will help you should you need to visit the hospital. Or maybe you enjoy watching a flood of trauma victims being transported precariously with various tubes sticking out of their bodies and go for the viewing pleasure? As sad as that sounds, it is better than being the patient.

1. Don't expect any progress in finding a 'cure' or an answer to your illness.

I think I have made this pretty clear from my paragraph above. I know how dismal this sounds, and, quite frankly, it's depressing. TV shows and documentaries want the population to trust hospitals; however, most doctors do not know what is wrong. It is called the "practice" of medicine for a reason. They have a grocery list of terms, symptoms, diseases, syndromes, etc., that they have memorized. Think of your favorite song. Mine happens to be "Little Lies" by Fleetwood Mac. Weird, you say? I don't see it that way! Just like you and I have memorized our favorite song lyrics, doctors have their lists memorized. When the first visit with our doctors' takes place, they perform standard evaluations. They will bob in and out of consciousness, only picking up words we say that light up their bingo charts. Take this conversation I had with an emergency room doctor, for example:

"I have difficulty keeping food down. I get quite dizzy and faint often. I am suddenly unable to read because the ordering of letters in words changes, and I am extremely paranoid, to the point where I can't trust going to the bathroom in my own house by myself without my mom inspecting the hallway beforehand."

A typical doctor will do the following:

...........difficulty keeping food down.... dizzy/faint........ dyslexia....... paranoid......... weird teenage girl paranoia.........

This is what our doctors interpret and internalize as they pretend to nod and stare at us reassuringly. Pro tip: They are just as clueless as you are.

2. Always, always, always remember what you've had to eat that day.

For some reason, nurses and doctors are forever blaming patients' diets. I happen to have severe food allergies that eliminate most of a standard American diet. That doesn't mean I'm malnourished, although one doctor was pretty convinced I was:

Doctor: So, sweetie, what have you had to eat today?

Me: I just told you, I can't keep anything down. But I tried to eat a hard-boiled egg, some cantaloupe, and a few crackers.

Doctor: Hmm. That isn't enough; it's already 4:30 pm. You should try to eat more. How about some milk?

Me: I'm allergic to dairy.

Doctor: I think that might be the problem.

That might be the problem?! I think we all know that people with known allergies don't go around consuming foods that restrict their airways. I mean that may just be me, but....I'm just saying.

Me: And how would my dairy allergy be the problem? (I ask this as though I believe the doctor, when I know it's complete BS.)

Doctor: Well, studies have shown that a decrease in dairy in one's diet can lead to brittle bones—

Me: I take a calcium supplement every day.

Doctor: Well, other studies have shown that those who choose not to drink milk—

Me: I am not *choosing* not to drink it. I'm allergic; there is a difference.

Doctor: Ok; well, studies have shown that the human body needs milk; otherwise, it can cause dyslexia.

Me: I don't mean to be rude, but even I, a high school sophomore, can tell you that what you just said makes absolutely no sense whatsoever.

Doctor: The studies have proven this, sweetie, and the results don't lie. Other scientific studies have shown—

My Mom: Ok, thank you, doctor; we appreciate your help, but I think we are going to explore a different specialist.

The same monotonous spiel about my diet—or lack thereof—was given to my parents and I more times than I care to count; so often, in fact, that the words seemed automatic, as if being read off a teleprompter. My doctors were terrible at acting like they knew what the hell to do. Again, it's the practice of medicine—right?

20

After my mom and I left the hospital that first time, we were utterly dismayed. We had false expectations about doctors that were put in place by society and television. Our experience brutally shattered them. (Clearly, not every doctor is as compassionate and curious as the actors are on Grey's Anatomy!) We had put so much emphasis and hope into this emergency room visit only to realize that we were more clueless than we were before we went.

So there we were, sitting in our car in the jam-packed hospital parking lot at 6:15 pm. As we scratched our heads, we wondered aloud what to do and where to go next. My mom had more confidence than I had that a solution was near. She always seemed to keep an even keel at all times—even when a hurricane lingered in the harbor. She knew a lot less about what my actual symptoms were, but that was all my fault. I wanted her to know. I wanted everyone to know. I wished I could have climbed up to the hospital roof and screamed for all the world to hear, but something deep inside blocked me from being able to tell my mom. It had transformed from an earlier fear of being classified as insane to suddenly realizing as I looked down at my hospital wristband in the dimmed sunlight of that painful afternoon that I was, indeed, crazy.

21

"I'm a 16-year-old teenage girl. Unfortunately, at least in my scenario, that means that I fall under the stereotype of being insane, right? With our hormones raging and all, teenage girls can be rebellious, obnoxious and, therefore, emotionally unstable. So categorizing myself in that way isn't that big of a revelation, is it?"

My therapist sat across from me and crossed her legs as if preparing to tune me into the reality that I was insane—literally, and not just hypothetically—like the example I used above. It is a precarious and delicate line for psychologists to diagnose an individual with insanity. They are trained not to overreact or give too much personal advice, which seemed impossible in this situation.

"Well, hmm, ok. Yes, you do make a solid argument that in today's society teenage girls are sometimes considered "insane" because of their actions…"

"So that means I'm right?!"

"Not too fast, Lauren. I do believe that part of what you are currently experiencing is a phenomenon stemming from this societal norm. However, considering all the symptoms you have discussed with me here, I have reason to believe that you are ill."

Ill. One word can wreak so much havoc on the mind, and this one did that to me. The funny thing is I never mentioned *him* in my appointments with her, so I could only imagine her response if I ever told her. "Surely, Lauren, you are delusional, coupled with a severe case of psychosis," she would say. The next morning I would wake up in a room with padded walls and an intercom in the far-left corner of the room as my only means of communicating with the outside world. I couldn't end up that way, but my mind wandered off on tangents whenever I heard that word.

As a family, we decided it would be best if I were to visit my dad's gastroenterologist for a second opinion. My faith was restored again, as I had visited this doctor several times, and had marveled at the intelligence and creativity he possessed. He gave my father his life back after several years battling ulcerative colitis, so surely he could help me. My father had a long history with doctors, and he would only go to those who were willing to work and listen to his opinion. Not surprisingly, such doctors were hard to find.

My dad wasn't diagnosed correctly with this autoimmune disease until his late 30s. At that time, medicine was not as advanced as it is today (or by the time you are reading this book), so his options for remedies were limited. He, too, experienced extreme denial from everybody, including his own family. *Sure, Dad, bringing rolls of toilet paper to work and returning home empty-handed is normal.* Through trials and tribulations and lots of error (lots and lots) he was able to find a biologic that gave him his life back: Remicade. It's been seven years since his first Remicade infusion, and it has been smooth sailing ever since - for the most part.

His story gave me hope that I, too, would eventually be diagnosed appropriately, given a biologic, and then my life would return to being peachy keen. Denial, it's not a river in Africa, and

it's more potent and powerful than any drug in the pharmaceutical field.

22

Booking the appointment proved more daunting than expected. We couldn't get in to see my dad's doctor, so we settled on seeing the physician's assistant the following week. She had the proper credentials and seemed very friendly, so I was willing to give her a shot. There wasn't much to lose at this stage of the game.

My mom dropped me off that Sunday evening at my dorm and, unbeknownst to me, she had brought a doggie bag full of my favorite dinner: chicken, rice and black beans with lime tortilla chips. The savory aroma floated throughout the air and satisfied the little part of my brain that still recognized happiness. It was tempting, but I couldn't eat it. I smiled, hugged her, and expressed my appreciation for the dish, but as soon as she left and the elevator doors shut, I gave the bag to a teammate rooming on the floor beneath me.

I hadn't eaten since dinner the night before. I hadn't vomited or had diarrhea since the night before, either. I was starving, but my body enjoyed the tranquility of not having to reject fuel. I read online that a human could survive on water for 30 days. I also learned that malnutrition and extreme heat are a recipe for death. Either way, death seemed like the only reprieve. The clock struck midnight, both figuratively and literally. Then it commenced: the marathon race to escape death.

The sound of my alarm clock was unwelcoming that Tuesday morning. On most days, this was the norm, but today it signified the first day of the first chapter on my quest for wellness. I had mixed feelings about the day. On the one hand, I would inch closer to a possible answer, but on the other, I would inch closer to knowing the truth. Would they tell me I'm actually dying? Did I have the emotional stability to accept the news? No, of course not. I don't know if anyone here on planet earth can accept that they are going to die—except for *him*. *He* was capable of just about anything, and that morning being no exception.

He passed by my dorm parent without notice and opened my dorm room door. I had no idea how, considering he'd need access to my key, which I had on me at all times. By the furrowing of his eyebrows and his quick pace, I could tell he had something urgent on his mind. He walked quickly to my desk and pulled my chair out into the middle of the room so he could see my face as I sat upright on my bunk bed. Throwing my books and notes on the floor, he sat down with a sudden *thump* and crossed his slender legs.

"Morning, Lauren."

"Hey, you seem on edge. Is everything alright?" I asked, grabbing my glasses so I could see him more clearly.

"Look, I know you have high expectations for today, but please don't expect much."

"Well, you're quite the negative Nancy."

"Seriously, Lauren. I know we have come a long way from our first introduction, and I am proud of that progress. But we have a long way to go before the truth is revealed, and I want you to understand that you need to have patience."

"How am I supposed to have patience if I am dying?"

"No one ever said you would die quickly."

Silence fell upon us as I crawled down my bedframe to the floor below. My muscles tensed and eased with each step I took. The knife-stabbing pain in my feet reappeared, along with the jolting spasm down my spine. I began to brush my hair, dutifully trying to ignore him as well as the pain. However, the pain intensified, along with a headache around my eyes. I felt light-headed and my heartrate began to accelerate. The room grew narrower with each uneven breath I took. I reached my hand out to stop the wall from inching any closer when my phone buzzed. It startled us both, but more so him, because my apparent psychosis entranced him. It was my Mom. I pressed the home button to unlock my phone and saw a screen filled with jumbled letters. *Essmaeges, iarfaS, Nboix, Martgitnsa*...I knew they were apps of some sort and nothing more. He asked me if I wanted him to read the message out loud to me, and I, of course, said *yes*.

"Lauren, sweetie, I hope you're awake. Today is the day!! Can't wait for my girl to get relief!" 6:26 am

He put my phone down on my bathroom counter as he noticed my face beginning to swell. He reached out his arms and I walked into them as though I were walking into the arms of death itself. They seemed so comforting and, as the tears fell onto the floor below, the only words left for me to utter were "It is only day one."

23

I managed to eat half an almond butter and jelly sandwich without any alarm. Therefore, I considered the day a success, regardless of what would happen later at the gastroenterologist's office.

I wore my lounge pants and a baggy t-shirt from a previous golf tournament to conceal my boney figure. It was apparent to those around me that I had lost some weight and, since I was an athletic, 5'2, 120-pound golfer, I didn't have much weight to lose. My efforts went to waste when I stepped on the scale in the nurse's station. 114 pounds. The nurse tried to hide her judgmental expression from my view, but I managed to catch it before she turned away. I knew what she was thinking, and it was, of course, untrue. I didn't use Weight Watchers; I used Jenny Craig. All kidding aside, my new lifestyle wasn't a get-skinny scheme. Concern fell upon my mom's face as the nurse marked down my weight in my file.

We turned, and the nurse gestured for us to follow her down a long, narrow corridor to the fourth exam room, where we would spend the next forty-five minutes waiting. The tension grew to the size of an eight hundred pound gorilla. My mom and I waited silently, listening to the sounds of people bustling about outside the room. Occasionally, we'd overhear a doctor speaking to a patient in the other exam room about how to prepare for a colonoscopy. To me, this seemed a bit redundant, considering all the posters that lined the walls. Graphic images of the large intestine, color-coded by region, and three dimensional figures of stuffed polyps and ulcers were just a few of the creepy decorations that lined the windowsills, but the crème de la crème had to be the program on the TV monitor narrated by a talking ileum, which spoke about the right and wrong foods to eat if you have IBD.

None of it amused my mom. Her face tensed with every breath she took, and with each exhale, she shrugged her eyebrows in apparent disbelief over something she saw on her phone. I knew it was the weight, and I knew why.

In middle school, food plagued me. I found it challenging to eat anything without having an episode, so I began to record my food intake every day until I had a long enough journal to document which foods caused the upset. It eventually got to the point that, once I had eliminated most of the food pyramid, I felt comfortable eating again. Shortly afterward, we found out I had food allergies, and it seemed to mitigate the problem. My mom's facial expression was akin to my medical mystery from three years ago, and I knew her thoughts followed. I thought the same, too, for a while; that is, until *he* came along.

* * * * *

The physician's assistant gave a semi-convincing nod along with an "I-don't-know-what's-wrong" stare for most of the appointment. I could tell that the list of symptoms alone was too much for her brain to process. It's as if I had told her I had flippers for feet; she would have been just as surprised by that.

My mom and I walked out of the appointment feeling better than we did that evening we had come out of the hospital, but so much still left unanswered. On the positive side, the PA prescribed me an anti-spasm medication that she said would help with the vomiting and would allow me to eat solid meals again.

We hoped this prescription was going to help me, but it certainly was not an answer.

24

The following morning I stumbled across campus to make the bus on time. It was a course day, meaning my golf group played a full 18 holes on a local course. School started at 1:00, so we departed campus at around 7:15 am to ensure we could play through and have enough time to come back, eat, and change for classes. My mind was non-functioning as I sat obeying and listening to my coaches speak about which skill we would be practicing on the course. I became like the doctors and nurses who nodded their heads with compassion and empathy but understood absolutely nothing.

The first nine flew by in a flash, and suddenly I stood on the eleventh tee, waiting for the group in front of me to play out. It was an unusually chilly day. November in Florida is much like any other month: hot. That day, however, I remember a pleasant breeze following me around the course. It was refreshing, especially when I had a moment to pause and wait. I took it upon myself to eat a granola bar and an apple; those anti-spasm meds did work, and I had started to resume my regular dietary habits. But something felt off. As I went to tee up my ball, an overwhelming sense of exhaustion came across me, and I struggled to keep my eyes focused on the shining white ball of light below me. It shifted positions, and I had to readjust my alignment each time the ball moved. After a while, it made me quite dizzy. I heard my coach and my group mates yelling and conversing, but all the words jumbled together until they sounded like a foghorn.

I didn't feel right, but I just needed to hit the shot; then I would sit down and tell my coach I needed to stop. My eyes began to close as I started my backswing. As my downswing approached, everything went dark.

* * * * *

Lights flickered above. My mom sat to my right, and there were nurses scattered around. I reached up toward my head to try to figure out what was on top of me, but a bunch of people in blue scrubs forced my hand down before I could touch my forehead. My mom stroked my hair and squeezed my hand tightly; tears stained her cheeks. I did not know what was going on or where I was at the time, but my body felt extremely cold and calm. The last thing I could remember was attempting to hit my drive on the eleventh hole. What had happened between then and now? Was this the following day, or am I missing school? The thought of missing school exacerbated my stress because I had to take my AP Biology and AP Language unit tests that day. Frantically, I scanned the room to find a clock. Scanning and searching through the many medical professionals scattered about, I began to realize I was in the nurses' station at school—or so I thought, until I read the sign 'TRAUMA' above the sliding glass doors ahead. They were the same doors I had just walked out of, so distraught, only a week ago. *What in the hell happened? I CAN'T be here again; these people know nothing! They are going to do more harm than good. I bet I am missing a test for AP Biology right now. Why am I stuck here?* As these thoughts rushed through my mind, I tried to maneuver myself up, but my mom shrieked in fright, and a herd of nurses rushed back to my side. *No, NO. I am leaving. I am exiting this place, taking my tests and never coming back to this place of infinite hell ever… FOREVER…*

"—grab the paddles, stat, and charge to 100. She's going into AFIB… NOW!"

There is an instant when your heartbeat stops and your body prepares to die. Yes; you do see a bright white light, but before that, I saw my life. I saw *all* of my life, to be exact. I saw my first bike ride through the sleepy suburbs of my hometown and the time I broke my ankle falling off a swing set in the 5th grade; I saw myself running in a field of flowers with my dog Charlie; and I saw myself all the way up to the present day, cold to the touch and surrounded by a wailing mother and panicked doctors. I had not looked as peaceful as I did in that moment for weeks. I walked over and touched my hair as I tried to listen to my mom speaking through her tears. She told me she loved me and that everything would be ok. She told me it wasn't my destiny, but was it? *He* had told me I was going to die soon; was this it for me? Of course, I did not want to die. I was only 16, and my life had just begun. I had big plans to see the world and help those less fortunate than me. But only the good die young.

25

I could see the beginning of the white light surrounding me, and I knew I would walk towards it when it came. But something stood in front of it, blocking my vision. *He* walked next to me and put his hands around my shoulder. No, it wasn't the grim reaper; it was *him*.

"Why are you here?" I asked. "You told me I was going to die soon, so I'm assuming this is my time?"

I stood just behind my parents. Both were sobbing and reminiscing about their favorite memories of me, wishing they had known what was going on sooner. I wanted that, too. I felt the squeeze of my mom's hand three times on my lifeless wrist. *I love you, also, Mom.*

I couldn't bear to look at the scene any longer, or to watch the two people I love most suffer over something that was out of their control. Stepping out of the room, *he* followed behind me, and we walked down the narrow, white-walled corridor together.

"Look; when I said you were dying, I never specified that indeed you *would* die," *he* began.

"Well, what exactly *are* you trying to specify, then?" I asked, puzzled.

"You need to wake up, Lauren. This journey is only beginning. I can't promise it will be a short journey and, hell, it certainly will be far from easy, but this is not your time to go."

I was amazed that, after all the difficulties he put me through, I was still listening to the words that fell from his mouth. He wasn't God; how could he possibly know my life's plan? But of course, the naïve and terrified girl inside of me clung to his words, as they were the only words of truth in my life.

"Wait; wake up? I'm on life-support. I can't magically snap my fingers and wake up a healthy person..."

"Lauren, wake up," he demanded again; but this time with a cheerful smile.

And like a metamorphosis, I arose. As my eyelids fluttered open, my coach's frazzled face came into focus.

"She's OK!" he exclaimed.

Suddenly, I felt the force of all my groupmates pulling me off the ground and onto a cart. One grabbed an ice pail, stuffed ice cubes into a towel, and placed it behind my neck, while another simultaneously placed an umbrella in front of the cart to safeguard my body from more sun exposure. I could hear echoes and murmurs of kids from other groups, but my body was in too much shock to process all of the sensory information.

"Lauren! Hey, Jesus...way to give an old man a heart attack. Are you all right?" My coach's voice was almost inaudible over the hollering of the other students on the course.

Positioning myself to see my surroundings, I familiarized myself with where I was and what I was doing before I responded. *I'm in Florida, this is a golf course, and I am a junior.* The reboot button on my flash drive slowly started to kick on.

"Umm, yeah; uh, I am good."

"Well, I think *good* is a bit of an overstatement at this point, but I'll take it. Hey, your mom is on her way out. One of the other coaches is giving her a ride to the hole in a cart, and she'll take you home, ok?"

"Ugh. Shoot."

"Um, what, Lauren?"

"Oh, nothing; I just forgot to finish a problem set for AP Biology; nothing big."

"Of course. You are the only kid I know who would freak out about a homework assignment after they just fainted from heatstroke. Good to know you're back, kid."

The only problem I needed to solve was how to convincingly tell my parents that I was indeed ok when I was not. I began to run several plausible scenarios through my head to explain what happened before my mom came.

Too much sun exposure… not enough sunscreen… I did not bring enough snacks…

I came to realize quite quickly all of my excuses sucked, so I resulted to the oldie but goodie excuse: the flu.

My mom was sobbing and terrified, just as she had been in my imagination when I blacked out. My coach and my mom carried me over to the cart while another coach grabbed my bag and belongings. I tried to voice what happened, but my attempts to speak were met with hushing and ice towels placed over my face. No; I wasn't dying, but it sure as hell felt like it.

The topography of the course was not in my favor; with each sharp turn the cart took, the acid in my stomach rose. Thankfully, we returned back to the clubhouse quickly. I felt as though

I was going to projectile vomit somewhere in between the cart and the car. My mom and the coaches exchanged relieved fare-wells as I looked on from the back seat. Maybe it wouldn't be so bad after all, and my parents would think that I needed a few days of rest. Whatever the outcome may be, I did not know. But there was one thing I did know for certain: vomit mixed with hormonal sweat is not a pleasant aroma.

26

The next event I remember was a trip back to the gastroenterologist's office. We were meeting with the physician's assistant again. My parents told me that they wanted to ask why in the hell I had fallen unconscious, but they claimed that they needed a new prescription for my anti-spasmodic medication. The medication didn't work well, except for the fact that I could eat without vomiting. Well, ok, it did work, but it didn't stop the "source" of my illness. It helped me stay alive. My family and I subconsciously knew that my health was much worse than needing a different anti-spasmodic medication. We weren't ready to unravel the mystery yet. Ok, that's another lie – *I* wasn't ready.

I had fallen into a vicious cycle of lying about my physical and mental health to my parents. I hate to say it, but it became second nature to me. At this point, in early November of 2016, my parents were absorbed in the upcoming presidential election and, thankfully, this diverted the spotlight off of me. So I did the same; I withdrew from talking and only spoke of school events or my updated college list. It wouldn't be long before my parents realized the extent of my deteriorating health, but at that moment, it felt nice to be in la-la-land.

The only person who understood the depth of my misery was *him*. It's ironic, I know, considering he first wanted to kill me, but friendships can develop in the most unexpected situations. He was there during my most trying moments like when I lay naked on the tile floor of my bathroom clutching the bottom of the toilet praying that I wouldn't see more blood come out of me. When my legs fell numb, and I stood awkwardly in the school hallway waiting to regain feeling, or the times I ran crying to the bathroom because the words on my exams kept switching order, and I wanted to give up. *He* never faltered. His visits were infrequent at first, but he eventually accompanied me everywhere, every day. We both agreed that I needed to tell my parents, but telling them would not be a natural act. It's difficult to tell someone you're suffering from something when you don't have physical evidence of ill health. The physician's assistant argued this point violently.

"Look; I have given hundreds of Dr. K's patients dicyclomine, and not even one person has ever reported this type of reaction. Dicyclomine is a very mild drug, and an episode of fainting could not be due to this drug. It was probably just heat stroke."

A look of disgust fell upon my mom's face. It wasn't just any look; it was the *asshole-you-have-no-idea-what-you-just-said-my-daughter-is-suffering-and-you-are-responsible-and-I-will-fight-you* look.

"Quite frankly, Ellen, I don't give a damn that none of the patients have had this reaction my daughter has had. You are not going to tell me she fell unconscious and has a constant resting heart rate of 110 because of 'light heatstroke.' This is not normal. Do *you* think this is normal? NO, IT'S NOT. My daughter is a stellar athlete and a phenomenal student, and she is not asking for any of this! She is losing weight faster than any diet I've ever been on, and yet she is always hungry. She didn't have any weight to lose in the first place! She is skin and bones. I've had it about up to HERE, because I know she isn't telling me the whole truth, and it's probably because of neophytes like you, doubting everything she says and never actually listening to her symptoms!

There is something wrong. I want to schedule a colonoscopy – NOW.

My dad and I locked eyes and gave each other the "damn she's out to play" glance. Ellen stuffed all my papers into my file and gave my mom a questioning look. Ellen could not have cared less about my mom's tirade. My mom stood in the opposite corner, proud of her rant, and in her fight position. It felt akin to watching a cheetah chasing a gazelle; it's terrifying for the gazelle, but you can't help cheering on the cheetah, because it is on a roll.

Ellen shifted on her stool and moved closer to me. I had an unnerving feeling wash over me. With one hand on my leg, she conjured up what seemed to be courage in the midst of my mom's reign.

"Sweetie, this year must be stressful for you, huh, with college looming and standardized tests…" she trailed off.

"Yeah…" I could tell by the condescending tone of her voice this conversation would not end well.

"Are you able to handle the stress ok? What do you like to do for fun?"

"How is this even relevant?" my mom interjected.

"Well, I'll just get to the point, then." There was a hint of bitterness in Ellen's tone.

"Lauren, maybe this issue isn't physical, or maybe it isn't an issue at all. Have you ever considered counseling or a short stay at a residential facility? I don't feel it's right to load you up on medication meant for someone with an *actual* illness, when your issues could be cleared up by some therapists and counseling."

"Actual illness?" She thinks I'm conjuring this whole thing up. Oh my god.

In that moment, I wanted to rip her head off her body and chuck it out the window. So did my mom, and she made that very obvious with the next slew of words that flew out of her mouth. I would include them, but I don't want to be too inappropriate, so I'll just include what I said. It took great force to say these words while anticipating the tears I knew would start falling any second, and I hate cursing in public, but ...

"Ellen, with all due respect, I'm not sure how you graduated from the empathy course in physician assistant training because you, ma'am, are an asshole."

I said it, and damn, it felt good. My mom and I both stormed out of the room as tears flowed down my face. My dad stopped at the front desk and made an appointment with the actual doctor. Enough was enough.

Now, there was obviously a lot more going on than I have described here. For instance, I had to undergo testing for various other illnesses. Practically every week I had another scheduled appointment at Quest Diagnostics in Lakewood Ranch. I'd been through a gauntlet of tests, most of which were inconsequential, because I knew they'd be negative. Celiac disease? Highly unlikely, considering I last ate gluten at nine years old. Type II diabetes? I couldn't eat chocolate because of the caffeine, and I despised candy. Type 1 diabetes? Negative.

The remainder of the tests were what the phlebotomists considered 'standard protocol,' comprised of a complete metabolic panel workup along with whatever disease they thought I might have contracted that week. The first time I had the panel done everything came back as **normal**. Ok, well, maybe it changes depending on my activity level. I grasped at any excuse to persuade myself that I wasn't manifesting these symptoms out of my own doing. The second week's report came back **normal**. The third week, **normal**. Fourth, **Normal**. Fifth, **normal**. **Normal, normal, normal**. I started to piece together slowly that maybe all of my symptoms were just a creation of my own doing. At least, that was the only valid explanation at this point. Every doctor I had visited thus far (four and counting) noted nothing wrong with my reports or tests. Even Dr. T told me that stress could cause wacky things to happen. Was this all just stress? Did stress cause me to see *him*?

"No, Lauren. I'm not from stress, and you know better than that. You're sick," he exclaimed in an irritated manner, interrupting my thought process.

He sat in the same place we first met— on the blush-pink, straight-backed chair. He fixed his tie so its grasp wouldn't be so tight around his burly neck. His nostrils flared as the knot did not cooperate in the manner he would have liked. Eventually, he gave up and, in doing so, he lost grip of his tie and flicked himself in the chin with one of his fingers.

"Ouch."

I tried to hide my smirk as he quickly flashed his eyes in my direction.

"Oh, be quiet, you. I didn't laugh when you walked into that wall yesterday."

Yeah, that happened. And no, I wasn't the typical millennial walking with their phone glued to their hand. I did not see the wall. My vision had been declining—rapidly, I might add, and I relied mostly on him to help me walk between classes at school. He thought it would be hilarious if he did not say anything to me when the white cinderblock wall approached me, and I hit it. He didn't laugh, but I'd never seen him smile so widely.

"Ok, fine; you didn't. I'll stop. But seriously, this can't all be in my head. It feels too real," I continued.

He got up, walked to my bed, and sat down on the edge, placing his arm around my shoulder.

"Listen, this isn't a figment of your imagination. This illness is the real deal."

"Then why do all my tests come back normal?"

"When have you ever been normal?"

And with that, he was gone.

27

My mom picked me up early from school that day. Usually, I'd be upset about missing class, but that day, I could not have felt more relieved. In less than twelve hours, I'd have a tube with a camera shoved up and down both of my ends. Oh, joy. The visual disturbed me but, for the first time in months, I genuinely felt happy. I believed that this test would yield the magical answer I needed. I'd be prescribed a miracle drug, and my life would be *forever* changed. Easy as 1, 2, 3. Ha; sure, Lauren.

A bit of the happiness subsided when I took a sip of the horrid concoction the doctor prescribed for me: two sixty-four-ounce containers of a laxative. I had to drink this medication to prepare for the colonoscopy and endoscopy. Have you ever tried dirty gym socks mixed with Robitussin and vomit? I do *not* recommend it. It was only my first swallow, and I also had another sixty-four-ounce container that I had to drink at 4:00 am. A long night was in store.

Despite crapping my brains out, my family tried their best to make the night as comfortable and enjoyable as it could be. We played Scrabble, watched an episode of Bull, and played blackjack. My parents both crashed on the couch around 11:00, which meant *him* and I would ride solo for the next five hours. I persuaded *him* to help me prepare for the Biology test I had on Thursday, convinced that I would be back to health after my colonoscopy on Wednesday. He knew I was delusional, but nevertheless continued to help me review for my exam.

The chapter test covered everything we learned in unit one, which included polymers, isomers, structural isomers, cis/trans isomers, carbonyl and carboxyl groups, monosaccharides, disaccharides, carbohydrates, lipids, and fatty acids. I had a high confidence level regarding the actual material the test covered. My heart sank when I remembered that my teacher would deduct points for each misspelled word. I had trouble remembering how to spell my name, let alone a five-syllable word. Up until this point, I had been using phonics cards I bought off Amazon my first week in the dorm. *He* suggested it would be a better idea if I tried to sound out the words as I wrote them. Initially, he wanted me to write down each term on its own separate flashcard, but considering we only had five hours before I crashed from exhaustion, he spared me and wrote them himself.

He shuffled the flashcards sufficiently before putting them behind him. He slowly reached behind his back and pulled a card ever so gently, so he wouldn't saturate the card with the oil from his finger.

"Ok, your first word is *carbohydrate*. I want you to write down your answer on this loose-leaf paper here, and we can sound it out together. Ok, Lauren?"

"Ok…," I replied timidly.

"Car."

"Car got it. C-A-R."

"Great! Ok, Car-bo."

"C-A-R-B-O-W—"

"No, Lauren; there isn't a *W* in the word. It is just "b-o."

"Ok, C-A-R-B-O."

"Yes, perfect. Ok; Car-bo-hy."

I wrote down *carbohl*. I frequently mixed up *y and l* in text-books, and it carried over to my spelling.

"No, Lauren; it's a *y* like *yarn*."

"C-A-R-B-O-H-Y."

"Yes! Ok, car-bo-hy-drate."

I wrote down *Drake*, as in the boy's name and the rapper who is obsessed with owls. I had a tendency to mix up letters when writing, and unfortunately on large unit tests like this one.

"No, Lauren; not the rapper. It is a *t* like *turtle,* not *k*."

"Ok. So the whole word is *CARBOHYDRATE*?"

"Yes. Here, write it out for me on the back of the flash card."

I stared at the card for a solid ten seconds before I remembered the task at hand. *Right, I can write the word – I've got this.* Car-bo-hy-drate. I enunciated each syllable as I traced the outline of each letter on the card. I handed the card back to him and he looked at me with a melancholy expression.

"Lauren, do you believe you spelled the word correctly?"

"Yeah, I sounded out each syllable and I separated the word into fragments, making it easier for me to spell, but I am not 100% confident in my spelling. I'm not 100% confident in anything right now, but I would give myself a 60% confidence rating for my ability to spell this word." It was astonishingly difficult to pretend I was joking, but he read right through my lies.

"Lauren, you spelled the word *Cerbahidrete*."

We looked at each other, and I lacked the courage to say what we both thought. I knew my troubles were ridiculous. I knew the onset of dyslexia was nearly impossible at my age. My illness caused this, but acknowledging it would validate its presence.

He then said all that was left to say:

"You have to acknowledge that you're gravely ill, Lauren; isn't this proof?"

28

"Let's get this shit show on the road! Oh wait; you don't have any shit inside of you – hah!"

I could always count on my dad to make grave attempts at a pun, even at my own expense. Usually, I'd be laughing and encouraging him to keep prodding, but this morning I felt like a cartoon character who got hit by a coconut from a palm tree above—dizzy, lightheaded, and in complete awe of what had just happened. After sleeping for a total of four hours, I felt like a steamroller crushed me inside and out, not to mention that the last time I ate solid food was thirty hours prior. Soon, though, it would all conclude, and we would have our answer to the mysterious symptoms doctors had no explanation for, including the rapid weight loss, and possibly even a reason for *him*. Within eight hours, my family would be able to rest easily, knowing what disease or issue may be lurking in my bowels. This sense of assurance kept me calm, even as the shallow pit of my stomach screamed for nourishment.

Within minutes, we were out the door and on our way to the outpatient facility. We tripled-checked that we brought all the necessary paperwork and, of course, food for my ride home. My nerves were on edge, set off by even the faintest sound of my mom swallowing her morning cup of coffee. The drive to the facility took approximately 26 minutes, but time played a constant illusion as I vacillated between staring out the window and eavesdropping in and out of my parents' hushed conversation.

My body sensed hours passing, even almost a day, but when I glanced at the clock underneath the front stereo, only four minutes had passed. *You've got to be kidding me.*

Inside the facility, the average age had to be around 63. Canes, dentures, and old lady perfume saturated the waiting room. I guess a teenager having a colonoscopy and endoscopy was not a common occurrence. My parents motioned for me to sit while they checked me in, and I promptly picked up a magazine before I laid down on a couch. It had something to do with gardening, but I couldn't grasp the full topic because all of the words were inverted. My exhaustion overwhelmed me, and I didn't have the time or the energy to play word scramble. I placed the folded magazine on my head to cover my eyes from the harsh interrogation-style lighting of the room so I could try to sleep; that is, until I heard the crystal-clear tone of my mother's voice.

"WHAT DO YOU MEAN YOU CAN'T PERFORM A COLONOSCOPY ON HER? MY DAUGHTER HAS BEEN FASTING FOR 30 HOURS, AND YOU'RE TELLING ME YOU CAN'T DO THE PROCEDURE? SHE ISN'T GOING THROUGH THIS HELL AGAIN. YOU'RE DOING THE DAMNED PROCEDURE."

"Ma'am, I'm sorry, but this center can only perform procedures on those 18 years or older. She is 16. I'm afraid the only place she can have a colonoscopy performed is at a hospital."

If the exhaustion, the hallucinations, and parched tongue weren't enough, now I had to deal with this. I clenched my jaw and kept my eyes closed, pinching my arm and telling myself it was a dream, but when my eyes opened minutes later, the same drab waiting room appeared before my eyes. *SHIT* was the expletive that ran rampant through my mind at that moment.

The sounds of my mom and dad arguing echoed throughout the boxed enclosure of the waiting room. My dad walked promptly outside to call the doctor as my mom bargained with the front desk receptionist. I should have known this experience was a sign of things to come.

My dad strode arrogantly back into the room and confided in my mom (for all to hear) that the doctor's office "forgot" that the outpatient facility does not take minors. He said his partner, a female doctor, would be able to perform a colonoscopy, but it would have to be at 6:00 pm at the hospital in Lakewood Ranch.

6:00 pm. The digital clock against the front entrance wall read 6:56 am. It would be another 10 hours at least before I could even have a morsel of food; not taking into account the possibility that the doctor may run late. Anxiety and terror collided as my mind spun out of control, and I began to worry about how I could keep my composure as my stomach ached for food. The clock became even more distant, and I began to sweat profusely, thinking about how I had to manage to stay afloat for another 10 hours. Wait; now it was 13?! The clock hands moved back to 3:56 am. Then 2:56. 1:56. 12:56. Dark black bubbles floated in front of my eyes as I grasped onto the sofa with my sweaty hands. *Ba-boom, ba-boom, ba-boom.* My heart rate steadily increased like the sound of a bass drum in a horror movie as the clock kept pushing back until finally, with a loud thump in my chest, the room went black.

29

"Minor, 16, fell unconscious in an outpatient facility. The patient is prepped for an exploratory colonoscopy and endoscopy. Bpm in the field was 185. Suggest alprazolam and steady oxygen until the procedure."

I remember two things from that day. The first being my parents supporting me on both sides of my body and carrying me through the brightly illuminated, barren hallways of the hospital. The second was lying on a gurney, hooked up to a bunch of monitors, crying hysterically. Like a baby wishing to expel the excess amount of gas in her system, I somehow hoped that crying would help me and stop the excruciating pain. It didn't help, but alprazolam sure did. Later I came to learn that alprazolam is the pharmaceutical name for Xanax.

* * * * *

I have a horrible history when it comes to sedatives, let alone prescription medications. When my body needs medical attention, and it receives a drug, (usually in the form of a pill), my body violently rejects it. My first experience with this reaction occurred when I had to get an MRI for my dislocated kneecap my freshman year of high school. Like most vertically challenged people, I am claustrophobic, and dread even entering an elevator with more than three people in it. Given my past medical history, my mom thought that it would be best for me to be sedated before the procedure to lessen my anxiety. She called my doctor, and she authorized a very, very small dosage of Valium. I was only 14. I see now that prescribing an addictive narcotic to a 14-year-old was utterly wrong, but that is beside my point here. My mom decided to err on the side of caution by giving me half of one pill instead of the full dosage. Thank G-d.

Thirty minutes after we arrived at the imaging center, I began hyperventilating and crying. I ran straight into the guest bathroom, locked myself inside, and pushed the cabinet against the door to barricade the only source of entry. That prompted a call to hospital security to come in and force me out of the bathroom. I'm assuming my knee healed adequately, but we'll never know.

*   *   *   *   *

The morning of a colonoscopy, you aren't even allowed a sip of water and, by the time we arrived at the hospital, it was 3:00 pm. My last glass of water was twenty-three hours earlier. I think you get my drift. Although my body felt calmer, my thoughts flashed back to the MRI experience, and my nerves suddenly felt on fire again. I tried my best not to focus on it and, thankfully, I succeeded as the exhaustion and drugs kicked in. I felt anxious, and then, suddenly, I didn't. I felt calm and peaceful as if I was floating on a fluffy white cloud – wait, is that a pink elephant?!

The second thing I remember from that day is the pink elephant. She seemed like a friendly lady, and she didn't mind me stroking or playing with her snout. Her voice was high-pitched, as if she lived on helium, and she wore a stethoscope and a white lab coat. She was very well put-together for a pink elephant, I might add. She told me the colonoscopy would go quickly, adding that I wouldn't feel a single thing. Then she came and unhooked me from all the various mechanisms and machines and wheeled me into the operating room. Her natural aroma of cotton candy and mangoes made me suddenly crave both foods as

I continued to pull and play with her snout. Once in place, she motioned the anesthesiologist to come, and he placed a snout (mask) onto my face. *How cool, I get one to match hers*! I thought. Then, as fast as it took to tell me to release her snout, I swiftly fell into a deep, forgetful, and blissful sleep. If the nurse at the Lakewood Ranch Medical Center reads this, I am so sorry for yanking on your lanyard and asking for cotton candy at least twenty times before my colonoscopy.

30

I never made it in to take my AP Biology test the following day. I didn't go to school for the rest of the week. Like everything else, I had an extremely delayed reaction to the anesthesia, which caused severe amnesia. The morning after my procedure, I could barely remember how to use the bathroom. For most of my waking hours, I pointed and drew things to explain to my mom what I needed. I'd point to a piece of fruit if I were hungry, and I'd draw (or at least try to draw) a picture of items found in my bathroom, so she'd know I had to go. I was completely bedridden and doubled over in inexplicable pain, which worsened every time I inhaled. The environment around me seemed to be constantly spinning, giving me an overwhelming sensation of nausea. *He* stood and sat and repositioned himself in different places around my room every so often, continuously chattering away about one topic or another. Was he this oblivious? He had soon developed into my aide, and when I needed him most, he ignored me.

As time slowly passed that day, my condition worsened. My bones felt brittle, and with every movement, even the short distance to the bathroom felt as if a thousand minuscule cracks erupted. It seemed as if I stepped on eggshells or a Lego. No, a Lego is more painful; it was definitely like stepping on a Lego. I went into the procedure and came out a different person: a chronically ill, disease-ridden person clinging onto the last string of her life.

Right before bed, my mom decided to read me one of my favorite childhood stories, *Goodnight Moon*. Yes, I was 17, but the body I lived in felt 85 years old, and the comforting memories associated with the book made me happy. She began to read and, slowly, my eyelids draped over my eyes. Soon, she finished the book and asked if I had to use the bathroom. I opened my eyes and flicked them around the room in confusion. *Who is this kind woman sitting in my bed, and why is she asking if I need to use the restroom?*

"Sure," I softly murmured. "But where's my mom?"

My mom bit her lip to stop from crying. It must have worked because I don't remember seeing her shed a tear. Later on, however, she told me that moment signified the beginning of everything to come and that she cried in her sleep, thinking she may not see me wake up the next morning.

Things escalated very, very quickly.

PART TWO

"As to diseases, make a habit of two
things – to help, or at least,
to do no harm."

– Hippocrates

31

"She should try the FODMAP diet. It will help with the bacterial infection—not as much as a course of antibiotics would, but due to her medical history and weak stomach, I'm going to advise that we try the alternative route."

Those were the words of the doctor who I thought would save my life from impending doom. The impending doom…of a bacterial infection?

"Are you sure she doesn't have irritable bowel disease? All of these symptoms seem quite rare for just a bacterial infection—the amnesia, nausea, difficulty remembering, and so on." My mom took a critical stance, detailing every symptom and medication I took after the bedtime story incident.

"We did see a few slight ulcerations in her small intestine and ileum, but they are so slight that the typical person would be unfazed by such ulcerations. Her presentation of symptoms and appearance is highly unusual for what I saw during the procedure."

"By her reactions to medications, we can tell my daughter is not in any way a typical patient," my mom replied slyly.

I glanced at my doctor and flashed her a look as if to tell her to proceed with caution, because she did not want to get on my mother's wrong side. Taking a second to re-angle her perspective, she spoke again. "Yes, I know, but I prefer we try another alternative route first. Pursuing other, more invasive options for

Lauren, based on these results, should not be done until all other, less invasive treatments have been tried."

The word "invasive" startled me. What could be any more invasive than a colonoscopy? It felt pretty invasive to me. I was sixteen, and I'd never even been kissed, and yet a whole team of doctors had seen parts of me I had never seen. Invasive seemed like a delicate adjective to use in this situation.

"What do you mean by invasive?" I asked, Interested in hearing my doctor's definition of this gently-used term.

"Well...if you don't respond well to the diet, I'd suggest we might have to do the pill-camera test and additional invasive blood work."

"Again, what do you mean by invasive?" I gawked, scared of what was about to come next.

"I mean invasive as in 19+ vials of blood drawn, Lauren."

Getting pricked by a needle by then was routine for me. My fear of needles waned by my constant exposure to them. Getting blood drawn was a regular occurrence; a routine consistent in a healthy human's week, like going to Starbucks. The sight of blood didn't scare me, and I enjoyed talking with the phlebotomists. Usually, they'd take about three vials, maybe four, and the rest of the day I knew I'd feel nauseous and lightheaded. Now, however, I'd have to multiply that feeling by nearly five times.

My mom and I left her office again, devoid of hope. Another dead end, another 'alternative route.' The feelings were all too similar, and yet, as with *him*, they were comfortable. My blood work didn't sound an alarm to death, and colon cancer had been ruled out, but still, his words lingered in my mind after each appointment: "You're going to die soon, Lauren."

Nothing in life is guaranteed, and I've learned that lesson by the large number of difficulties I had begun to experience, but knowing that my life may come to an end soon, I took it day by day.

32

When I returned home, my mom wrote down notes in her journal (more so *my* journal, since every symptom or illness I had ever experienced was written in that notebook. My mom called it "Lauren's Medical Mystery Book", and for $20 you could win an all-inclusive package to visit Lauren's grave! (Ok, too far. Sorry.)

I ventured over to my desk and wrapped my faux Sherpa blanket around me as if I were a burrito, turned on the Imperial March (aka the Death March—no pun intended here) full blast and began to research this elusive 'FODMAP diet.'

Within minutes, my mom beckoned from the other room. "Lauren, I know you're mad, but I can't listen to that for another nine hours. Not today. Put headphones in or close your door."

I have habits, just like everyone else. One of mine is playing the Death March song from *Star Wars* and wrapping myself up like a burrito in a blanket. I am Darth Vader when I'm raging mad. Sue me. It probably would be nine hours before I changed the song, so I went over and shut my door. I needed time to ponder while sitting in my Death Star.

As thirty minutes passed, the amount of information I'd collected on this FODMAP diet was the equivalent of a slice of swiss cheese to a wall mouse. Everything, from recipes 'do's and don'ts' for your first week, to current dieters' blogs about their experiences with the diet, to meal prep ideas. I suddenly felt confident that maybe I would be ok; that is, until I read what is allowed on the FODMAP diet:

- Veggies: eggplant, green beans, cucumber, lettuce, tomato, zucchini, potato, etc.

- Fruits: cantaloupe, grapes, kiwi, orange, pineapple, strawberries

- Dairy: (I'm allergic, so I skipped this section)

- Protein: Eggs, poultry, seafood

- Breads: (Allergic to gluten and cannot digest corn, so I also skipped this section)

- Sugars: dark chocolate

- Nuts: macadamias, peanuts, pumpkin seeds, walnuts

As I mentioned earlier, I am allergic to dairy, soy, gluten, peanuts, hazelnuts, alcohol (we'll get to that story later) and cannot, for whatever reason, eat sugar. From a very young age, I had gastrointestinal and digestive challenges when I consumed anything that contained a high sugar content, so I despised Halloween and any holiday that involved the delicious delicacy that is sugar. Sure, I could eat it, but the benefits of eating a candy bar did not outweigh the hours of pain I'd feel afterward, not to mention the sleepless nights I'd suffer through from one "fun size" Hershey's bar. To me, it just didn't seem worth it.

Within those thirty minutes, I also came to this realization: My daily diet followed the FODMAP diet. Sure, I had an occasional apple, which was considered "illegal", but I never ate anything else listed in the unlawful foods section.
Well, the boost of adrenaline and confidence was nice, but back to my reality…

33

"I just don't get it."

"What don't you get, Lauren?"

My frustration was apparent from my burrowed eyebrows and constant need to pick at my fingernails, while I sat crossed-legged on the nylon sofa in Dr. T's office. Dr. T. looked disinterested in everything I said but managed to appear enthused with a false façade. I glanced towards the shadow cast by the swaying palm tree outside her window. Birds fluttered in the air around the tree, and the sound of their chirping reminded me how much I missed nature—the sounds, sights, and smells. I paused and daydreamed longer than I should before I answered her.

"Well, I don't think you are insane, but you are at an age where hormones are raging, and sometimes they can throw things out of proportion."

"So you're saying that this could be a result of my hormones?"

Again, the beginning of another conversation with a health specialist that made no sense whatsoever.

"Well, no, and yes. Can you give me a walkthrough of your symptoms again, Lauren?"

"How much time do we have?"

"35 minutes; why?" she asked, curiously.

"Well, it's going to take that long to explain all my symptoms." And with that, her false façade fell, and her genuine emotions began to show. There was a look of hysteria on her face that felt all too common.

"Ok; starting from the top. Let's see…where to begin…oh, ok; well, it would be easier if I sort of bullet point each one, is that all right?"

"Whatever you fancy, Lauren." A hint of attitude inflected in her tone.

"Severe bloating, migraines at least 4-5 times a week, frequent urination, brain fog, nausea, joint pain, muscle pain, blurred vision, reorientation of words every time I read them, vomiting, heart palpitations, night tremors, nightmares, excessive sweating, ringing in the ears, poor balance and hand/eye coordination, a metallic taste in my mouth, loss of appetite, night sweats, swelling of the hands, feet, and jaw, chronic fatigue, forgetfulness, dizziness, nausea—"

"Ok, hold on Lauren. You're going way too quickly. My hand cannot keep up with everything you are saying. Now, you mentioned something about words being spelled differently each time you read them. How exactly does this present itself?"

"It started my first day in AP Biology. I flipped open my textbook, and all the words were jumbled. "Most" turned into "osmt" or "stmo" or "somt", and so on. At first, like a typical distressed teen, I blamed it on a miserable night's sleep, but the next day the same thing happened, and this time it crossed over to my spelling. I received my first quiz back, because I misspelled all of the terminologies incorrectly, my grade suffered. I apologized to my teacher several times before I glanced at the exam and noticed that everything looked correct to me. After that, I bought a set of phonics flashcards and a book of syntax off

Amazon. I've hidden it from my classmates and my parents. It's gotten much harder, though, as the vocabulary has increased in difficulty and length. Before I do any work, I take out the cards, lay them out in front of me, and trace the letters on each one. Most of the words are one syllable, but some of them are found in the vocabulary terms I'm learning, so I break the word into chunks and then memorize them piece by piece."

"How are your grades? Are you in contact with your counselor at all? Knowing you, maybe you should switch to a less demanding course than an AP, with your difficulties."

"What is that supposed to mean?" I had not let my vulnerable side show until now, and I immediately began to regret it. Did she think I was incapable or, worse, that this phenomenon I had been experiencing was my new normal?

"Well, I know how serious a student you are and, given the difficulties you are facing in school, your report card, for lack of a better word, probably isn't 'pretty'."

"I can pull it up for you if you'd like."

"Sure, I'd like to see it. Maybe you should bring this up to your parents' attention so they can source out help for you."

I slid my phone across the table, and this was the screen that showed:

Semester 1: AP Biology: B+

Pre-Calculus: A-

AP English Language: A+

Studio Art: A+

She shifted in her chair and pursed her lips, thinking of a retort to what appeared before her eyes.

"Oh. Never mind. You are quite a capable young lady. May I ask how you get these grades? How long do you study each day?"

"It certainly is a challenge, but I wake up at 5:00 am every day to study before practice if I can manage to go, and I study during lunch and up until about 9:00 pm when I crash. It's hard to make ends meet sometimes, but I talk to and visit my teachers every day during office hours and do most of my work then. After school, I dedicate the majority of my evening to my flashcards and syntax book; that is if I'm not vomiting or curled up in the fetal position on the bathroom floor from dizziness."

"You know, you are not normal, Lauren."

"I've been told that a few times."

With that, our session ended, and feelings of panic began to flourish inside of me. Yes, I knew I wasn't normal, per se, but was I supposed to be failing my classes? Maybe people weren't believing my "mysterious" illness because of my report card…and that's when it hit me: they think I'm faking it.

34

"Lauren, your Dad called his old gastroenterologist at Mt. Sinai in New York to get a second opinion, and he recommended a pediatric gastroenterologist. She's excellent—stellar ratings and reviews."

"Wait; um, okay, now?" I half-heard what came out of my mom's mouth, but I lip-read the rest as my ears rang like church bells on Sunday.

"Well, winter break starts next weekend, and Dad and I want to fly you up next week. She has an opening slot available because of a cancellation, and her next available appointment after this won't be until April. We need to take it, because we don't think we are going to get an answer for you here, L."

I agreed. Every path we tried to take led us back the way we came and straight back to square one. This FODMAP diet seemed less like an answer than a poor, uneducated guess designed to shoo away a patient with strange symptoms for which the doctor had no clue. I believed that eventually I'd wake up one morning and realize that everything I had experienced was just an illusion, but that seemed more and more unlikely with each passing day. The pain and symptoms were becoming too frequent and peculiar, and I didn't know what to think or who to believe.

* * * * *

From a young age, I had seen doctors as superheroes. To me, it seemed as though they were able to find an answer to every issue while simultaneously putting a smile on kids' faces. I wished that this definition of doctors was the rule. My feelings about them had become more negative. I viewed their intellect with suspicion, similar to the way I look at my dog when she chases her tail. I could not fathom how doctors' could allow themselves to give up on a patient when they accepted the task of doing their best the day they entered medical school. I knew, of course, that my case was an oddity, and clearly, not an easy one to handle, but wasn't that one of the allures of medical school—being able to help those who cannot help themselves? The image that I once held of doctors turned dark as I began to question everything that came out of the mouths of 'medical professionals.' *He* said I was going to die soon, and it was my job to make sure doctors' didn't make my passing happen any sooner.

* * * * *

We took the appointment. My mom booked us a flight, but she would not be able to come, as Christmastime travel is expensive. She figured that since my dad had a history of the disease, he'd be better suited to go with me, as he'd be more familiar with the terminology and medications the doctor may prescribe. Invariably, I had my hopes up, as I imagined this doctor to be the superhero that "saves the day" — and my life. It would not be long before I abandoned that train of thought altogether.

The night before our scheduled flight, my dad and I began to pack for our trip. Even though I felt less than optimal, my mom wanted us to spend a few extra days to be "tourists" and enjoy Christmastime in the city. I know she had the best of intentions and wanted to do something out of love, but I regretted the trip, as I just wanted to come straight back home. I asked her what prompted her to treat us, and she told me she had received my report card. I looked at it, the same letter grades I showed Dr. T, and I was still convinced that my school sent the wrong student's report card:

AP Biology: B+

AP English Language and Composition: A+

Pre-Calculus: A-

Studio Art: A+

Maybe I could handle the work-load, and I just psyched myself out. Or perhaps I was a super-hero in secret. I want to think the latter, but the first is more logical.

35

The next morning, as my mom barreled around the departures deck at Sarasota International Airport, I couldn't help but pay attention to the sinking feeling in my stomach. After seeing three doctors, my confidence in the medical community sat at an all-time low, but I still managed to appear hopeful. My parents had extended an opportunity, and I'd be an idiot not to take it. Of course, they wouldn't let me refuse to accept it. I stroked my dog Charlie's fur before we came to an abrupt stop (my mom is horrible at braking). As I exited the car, our goodbyes were swift as we were running late (as usual). I hugged my mom one last time before we ran to the check-in counter, and brushing the hair away from my left ear, she whispered, "It will all be ok." I clung to each word as if they were the last I'd ever hear from her.

Standing in line waiting for our plane to take off, I heard my name called over the intercom. My dad looked up from his *New Yorker* magazine and flashed his eyes in my direction. I walked over to the ticket counter and presented myself to the gate agent.

"Hi, Lauren. You are seated in an exit row. Will you be able to handle being an assistant to the crew in case of an emergency landing?" she asked.

HELL no! I thought to myself. Outwardly, however, I tried to show confidence by replying, "Sure; of course!"

"Great," she replied. Could you please just read the skew of numbers on the bottom right of your ticket so we can confirm your seating arrangement?"

I read the numbers off to her, but I must have jumbled them up as usual, because she gave me a quizzical look and said, "I'm sorry miss, but there should be a slew of numbers at the bottom right corner."

"Oh, yeah. Sorry, sure."

I repeated the same sequence, but in reverse.

"Miss, I can just take the ticket," she replied.

I handed the ticket over to the gate agent as she glared judgmentally in my direction.

"Sorry," I winced. "I forgot I don't have my contacts in."

I had just told yet another lie in a long series of white lies. As I turned away, I began to question my truthfulness, but more so my sanity.

37

Manhattan is a city where you can feel isolated and popular simultaneously. In New York, problems pale in comparison to everywhere else, and only in New York can you find the best of the best. By this, I mean the medical community, but this statement could also describe Chinese food (seriously; do try Chinese food in the city if you can). Top tier, renowned specialists from every field congregate in this metropolis, and New Yorkers and out-of-towners alike compete for appointments. Because my dad's former gastroenterologist worked at Mt. Sinai, he spoke to the doctor I had an appointment with on my family's behalf. I was able to make an appointment with this top pediatric gastroenterologist in her field quickly. If her office had not had that cancellation, the next available appointment would have been April 23rd, 2018 and it was now only December 22nd, 2017!

So began my first lesson in being a chronically ill patient: the medical system in America is corrupt. Doctors seem to be everywhere, in every corner of every town in every city in every state. After all, I pass at least three medical buildings on my commute to school alone. With chronic disease and illness, the number of medical professionals becomes skewed. 90% of the medical population cannot help the chronically ill because their training is not in a specific field. To make matters worse, being 16 made my experience even more daunting. Why, may you ask? Health insurance. Yes, wonderful insurance that is supposed to cover your medical costs made my journey even more of a living hell. According to our insurance guidelines, I was considered a minor as I was under the age of 18. But medical professionals didn't recognize me as a juvenile because I was less than two years away from being 18 (a "legal" adult). Pediatric doctors did not want me as a new patient, because in less than two years, they would lose me as a patient. The insurance companies wouldn't cover me unless a pediatric physician treated me. My mom spent hours pleading with different doctors' offices to take me as a new patient. One of the doctor's offices my mom had called said to her, "Your daughter would be a waste of our time because, in less than two years, she would age-out of our practice." Eloquently phrased, right?

Even when the odds seemed stacked against me and we finally found a doctor who would take me, I hesitated before feeling relief. "How long is the wait time for an appointment?" became such a common phrase that I felt like my vocabulary shrunk every day. My life turned into an ongoing battle of fighting to stay alive until the next day, let alone for the three to six months it could take to see a doctor. I call this wait time the 'holding pattern', because you are kept waiting by the medical community somewhere between life and death. I only know this now because, at this point in my journey, I was about to enter one.

37

Back in New York, my Dad and I settled into my mom's close friend's apartment as the sun started its descent across the skyline. I remember looking at my watch and doing a double-take because darkness began to creep along the horizon at 3:30 pm. Daylight savings time is much different in Florida. I hated daylight savings time, but it seemed rather fitting given my situation: living life in darkness.

Dinner time rolled around and my dad offered to grab Chinese food from our favorite place a few blocks away. As he shut the door, I walked over to the window seat twenty-nine floors above Central Park. The energy of the city below was contagious. I suddenly felt as if I needed to do something productive, so I decided to organize my weekly pill container before my dad came back. My daily regimen consisted of an anti-spasmodic, digestive aids, anxiety medications, and an allergy pill. It didn't take that much effort, but I became OCD about it, as my life revolved around the 8x12 inch plastic box. Without a digestive aid pill at each meal, I'd vomit, and without my anxiety medications, I'd hyperventilate at least four times a day (no exaggeration).

To any sane person, I seemed insane—and I was—but as with everything else, I did not want to live up to my frightening reality. By the time I had finished sorting my pillbox, my dad had returned with the Chinese food. I had ordered steamed chicken and vegetables, which is underrated. Sure, it may sound bland, but it's scrumptious. It's been my Chinese food staple for as long as I can recall. It's never disappointed me, so I've ordered it at every Chinese restaurant since. I don't like disappointment, especially when it comes to food, but things have changed. Now I have to choke down three digestive aid pills before I can even handle a few bites of food. When I do begin to eat, I have a hard time getting it down.

That evening, as I began to eat the steamed chicken and vegetables, the smell of the chicken started to make me nauseous, so I pushed the pieces of chicken off into the corner of my bowl. After 20 minutes, I had hardly touched my dish. Looking up, I noticed my father watching me uncomfortably.

My denial could not have been stronger.

38

"Rise and shine, sweet pea. We have to get going in about 30 minutes. I know I should've woken you up earlier, but I know you had a rough night, so I let you sleep late. Do you need me to get you anything?"

My voice croaked as I tried to process all the information my dad threw at me. I understood I had thirty minutes, but where were we going, and why had my dad's temperament changed? Also, why was there blood on my blanket? I'm not on my period, am I? I thought. I reached for my shorts and didn't feel a pad, so I thought I was ok.

"Lauren? Hey, sweetie, you awake?"

I completely forgot my dad was standing there beside the couch where I had crashed at about 3:30 am.

"Yeah…where are we going so early? Do you know why there is blood on my blanket?"

"Hon, today is the doctors' appointment. As for the blood, I don't know. Are you on your period?"

"No…" Considering I didn't know what day it was, that was a courageous question for my dad to ask.

"Well, I heard you get up and walk to the bathroom several times, so maybe you bled out a bit. It's ok. That has happened to me. Don't panic, honey."

Tears began to fall down my cheeks. My exhaustion and anxiety began to destroy me, along with the never-ending pain I endured every day. My dad sat down on the end of the sofa and grasped my feet beneath the blanket. He seemed annoyed and rightly so, considering my mental state, but he hid his frustration. He knew that morning was not my friend—or at least, that's what I told myself. In reality, he hid his annoyance because of my unknown illness, and it took just as much strength for him to fight back the tears as it did for me to release them.

"Sweetie, it will all be ok. Maybe not today, or even tomorrow, but I promise that eventually, you will be ok. Your mom and I are always here for you; please remember that, ok? Now, get up, and I'll make you a smoothie. Do you want strawberry-banana or banana-almond butter?"

I wiped my face as my dad continued to stroke my feet, but I couldn't imagine eating anything.

"I'll grab a coconut yogurt with some banana; thanks for the offer. I love you, Dad," I said, barely above a whisper.

"I love you, too." He grabbed my suitcase and put it on the coffee table beside me. "Here; just throw something on, and we'll get going, ok?"

As my thoughts shifted to the day ahead, I focused my vision on the large window on the other side of the room. I could see the expanse of Central Park and all the life that buzzed around it. It seemed too complicated, too loud, too busy for a girl like me. I picked up pieces of my clothing and shuffled it around my suitcase. My body felt discombobulated, like the articles of clothing thrown across my battered luggage. My body, like the suitcase, felt old and worn. Maybe it is my time to go. Perhaps I am not cut out for this life, I thought. I decided on athletic joggers and a long-sleeved purple t-shirt, and I finally felt okay with the fact that maybe soon I wouldn't be a part of this actively buzzing world. Isn't that what my body was trying to tell me?

39

Imagine a zoo. Imagine that each exhibit in this zoo had its own space and, within each building, there were multiple floors on which there were numerous exhibits. Now, imagine this zoo was in New York City and, instead of various buildings, there was only one. Welcome to Mt. Sinai, the medical zoo of New York City. As my dad and I walked the active halls, we kept getting caught off guard by the flow of people. Coming from a small Floridian town and not having lived in New Jersey for two years, we had grown unaccustomed to mass quantities of people. I held my dad's hand, afraid I'd lose him in the crowd and also because I was terrified. My palms grew increasingly sweaty with every step we took, and my heart rate seemed unhealthily high. I tugged on my dad's arm to make him stop because I wanted to see if we could find a restroom. He knew why, of course.

* * * * *

A few years ago, I self-diagnosed myself with sensory overload disorder (if that is even the proper term). Every time I found myself in a place with a lot of stimuli and movement, I grew faint and would eventually vomit. My family never knew what the root of my issue was, but a feeling grew inside of me that this journey I'd been forced to take would provide the answer. But for now, I needed to vomit.

* * * * *

"Ok, sweetie; I see one around the next corner. We'll stop there," he said, with his voice a decibel louder than average. People shuffled past us left and right as we continued to navigate the maze of Mt. Sinai.

When I saw the sign, I let go of my dad's hand and ran as fast as my little legs could propel me into the restroom. After the usual, I leaned against the wall and peered out of the pinhole-sized window next to the sink. Even more people, even more activity. I began to sob uncontrollably. I closed my eyes as I did when I felt overwhelmed, and I just stayed there in the tiny closet of a bathroom. The concept of time felt foreign to me, as the coolness of the subway tile fell upon my scalp, and my purple long-sleeved t-shirt, drenched with sweat, hung at my sides where muscle and body fat used to be.

I started to think about the remark the gastroenterologist in Florida made about how I may need some 'cognitive help,' and that my symptoms were just a byproduct of typical 'teenage stress.' Maybe she did have a point. People have called me high-strung throughout my life, and I never took pride in that matter, so perhaps I needed to change. My symptoms seemed to start at the beginning of my junior year, so there seemed to be a correlation. Without intending to, I was coming up with any excuse just to run from the truth of the matter. That's how my disease progresses. It makes its sufferers concoct alternative scenarios until, sooner or later, the reality inevitably hits them straight across the face. Or stone-cold, six feet under.

40

I opened the bathroom door cautiously, careful not to hit anyone on the other side. Trying to navigate my exit from the bathroom felt akin to crossing a four-lane highway, in which any sudden movement or misstep could cost one's life. My dad seemed unfazed by how long I had disappeared. I guess he had grown accustomed to it by now, given how often I used the restroom.

We managed to find the gastroenterology floor and sign in at the patient desk before sitting on a bench right underneath a giant window. Ironically, looking outside seemed to help whenever I had a panic attack, although 'outside' in New York City consisted of the real triggers that set off the panic attack inside: people and lights and activity and blinking and talking and smoking and pets and flashes. It was all just too much.

I lay under the fluorescent light fixture staring at the dead fly in the corner for over two hours. You could have told me a day had passed, and it would have felt the same to my body. Minutes morphed into hours, which morphed into days—it all blended to create a false mirage.

Two hours prior, when the nurse had led us into the exam room, I immediately went straight to the table and lay down. Quizzically, she asked, "Are you ok?" Of course, I wasn't; otherwise, I wouldn't have an appointment. Instead, I told her what I automatically said to other nurses: that 'doctors are never on time, so I might as well relax.' She seemed annoyed by my opinion, but something about her facial expression led me to believe I wasn't wrong. Two hours later and yet another doctor had proved my theory to be correct.

She came in promptly, without apology, and immediately asked for my 'story.' I regurgitated as much of my medical history as I could remember, and my Dad would interject and fill in the missing bits. She wore the same empathetic expression the other doctors had shown, and she gave an encouraging nod every few words or so. I saw right through her façade, however, and the glimmer of hope within me vanished. She was just another cog in the wheel. If that weren't enough, each time I would tell her stories about what I had been going through, she'd interrupt me. She would respond with patronizing statements like, "Oh, sweetie, that can't be happening to you at *your* age," or "Sweetie, what you said made no sense. You should have your facts straight first before you try to defend yourself." She would then place a hand on my knee, making me feel even more conscious and delusional than I did from her condescending attitude.

He sat beside me the entire time, and when I eventually realized the direction the appointment was heading in, I tuned her out and focused on him. He began to speak, but I didn't reply, because that would undoubtedly convince her of my insanity. My sanity was *still* not something I was comfortable letting go of—yet.

"Look; I hate to say this, but I told you so, Lauren. It is not going to be an easy task figuring out your illness. When I first appeared to you that morning in your room, I thought my best plan of action would be to awaken you to the reality of your situation and life would go back to being hunky-dory. I did not expect your health to worsen to the degree it has, and I am scared for what the future holds for you. I know I gave you that awful prediction, and I am not going to repeat it for fear of causing you more anger, but know that I am with you and that I will be here for you each step of the way. Sooner or later, we will stumble upon an answer together. I wish I knew why you had to go through this, but I don't. Just remember, I am here for you."

I knew the prediction he spoke of, but I was afraid that repeating it would make it come to fruition - something I desperately wanted to avoid. I tuned back into the conversation between my dad and the doctor, whom I'll call Dr. P, and I heard something that startled me even more.

"Well, maybe the pictures were inconclusive, given the events that transpired the morning of her procedure. Possibly the best plan of action is to schedule another colonoscopy, but instead of having it done in Florida, have it done in our facility. This way, I can guarantee everything goes off without any problems."

Another colonoscopy? I had to have misheard her. Those words did not just come out of her mouth. How could she expect me to have the procedure again, as though it were as easy as the drop of a hat? And for what? A higher resolution photo? I am not an intestinal model, nor did I plan to be one, and my body didn't take to this procedure willingly. It would take several pain-stricken days to prepare for the procedure by emptying every last morsel from my corpse-like body. I then would have to starve myself for twenty-four hours for a 45-minute procedure, leaving me bedridden for three or more days. I was defiant that I would not go through the procedure again and, thankfully, my dad was, too.

"I appreciate your input, Dr. P, but having Lauren go through this procedure is incredibly taxing on her body. If you are suggesting it for the sake of obtaining a slightly better quality photo, it seems ridiculous to put her through this. We already know that she doesn't have ulcerative colitis, but Crohn's could be any-where. Is there any way to look in her small intestine? Maybe the ulcerations are higher up, and the camera for the colonoscopy wouldn't reach it. In any case, she is not doing this procedure again."

I appreciated how civilly my dad acted. If my mom had come to this appointment, she would have ripped this doctor a new you-know-what. But I agreed that the stress I'd have to endure would not be worth it, and maybe another test existed that could view my small intestine further. I dunno. All I know is that the aroma of the burrito *he* was eating as he sat next to me on the exam table made me want to vomit.

Dr. P sat back, frustrated by my dad's lack of conviction in her opinion because she most definitely thought she was the 'gastroenterology god.' Her brows furrowed as she reviewed my paperwork again. Every few seconds, she looked at my file and then back to my dad and me. When she grabbed a pen from her coat pocket and starting writing notes, *he* whispered in my ear.

"I can see in your eyes you're getting your hopes up, and I want you to know that nothing is going to come of this. I hate to be blunt, but this is your reality, Lauren."

Dr. P sat up and re-crossed her legs. "Well, then. If you are **dead** set against repeating the procedure, I have nothing else to recommend but for her to try the FODMAP diet, and these is-sues should self-resolve. The only other procedure I can recom-mend is a pill-cam test, but given her present symptoms and the cost, it seems pointless to perform this procedure on her. If the diet doesn't work, give her some downtime, or have her talk to someone. I have a feeling that would help her."

In response, I said, "I have several food allergies for which I am already on a daily diet that is very similar to the FOD-MAP diet, and it isn't helping."

I could see the displeasure in her face. "Well, I don't know what to say to you. Best of luck, amd you and your wife should seek a psychotherapist for her to speak to." And with that, she shook my father's hand and walked confidently out of the room. As the door slammed behind her, tears began to fall in torrents down my face.

My dad rushed over to my side of the exam table and wrapped his arms around my head. He stroked my hair and patted my back as I tried to not choke on my tears.

"Hun, she's an asshole, ok? You don't need psychotherapy, and your mom and I know you are ill, ok? You don't have to prove yourself to anyone. We know our daughter best, and we know that this is something out of your control. We both were looking for more resolution today, and that didn't happen, which is unfortunate, but know that we are not going to stop until we have an answer, ok? We will get to the bottom of this and figure out what is wrong. It might not be today or tomorrow, but you will get better soon. Just like I said before, I promise."

A soft smile spread across my damp face. My parents' believed me; *he* believed me. I wasn't insane, and I was ill.

I wish I could have remained more optimistic throughout my illness, but hearing those words over and over made fighting for the next day less and less daunting. "You'll be better soon." *Soon*, it's a funny word, and maybe I had the definition wrong, but I thought *soon* referred to a time in the distant future, say, one day to a week, not two and a half years.

As for *his* words, I was already dying.

41

We had a few days left in the city before our flight back to Sarasota on Sunday. My dad and I wanted to take the little energy I had left after my appointment and channel it into something exciting, like visiting the new World Trade Center or taking a tour of NBC Studios. It was mighty ambitious of us, considering we barely slept; we were up face-timing my mom until the early hours of the morning. Both of us needed a distraction; however, a big one. I am not an emotional person, but when faced with difficulty, I do what is highly frowned upon by psychologists: repress my feelings. Each of us deals with stress in different ways. My dad can finish an entire season of *House of Cards* in a day, while I can read a whole series of soapy teen romance novels just as quickly. Perhaps it's not productive, but our goal is achieved: avoiding reality and the truth. We aimed to do the same today and for the rest of our time in the city. We had not formally spoken about the appointment since we had hung up with my mom. Somehow, silently, we agreed never to talk about the visit again. Usually, given the situation, we would go to the Bayfront and watch the sailboats along the harbor, but we were in New York City. We could do anything and everything, and we were determined to do it.

After breakfast and my dad's mandatory espresso (a must-have after practically pulling an all-nighter), we made a game plan. We decided we would go to the Museum of Modern Art that day as well as the REI in Soho. The next day we planned to tour NBC Studios and go to the NHL Store. The last day we'd spend in Central Park until the evening when we would go see the light show on 5th Avenue for Christmas Eve. We buzzed with excitement. The lack of an adequate amount of sleep left me suffering from the delusion that I'd be able to handle all of this, but at the moment, I wanted to live. I did not want to think about having to always be near a restroom. I tried to ignore my swollen my ankles and how I should be taking my antidepressants with lunch. For a few days, I did my best to ignore the pain and obligations of being ill and felt like a regular teenager.

It seemed to work, as I didn't stop once during our festivities to ask to go back to the apartment. Sure, I was running on pure adrenaline, but I didn't care. I had not felt as alive in months as I did then, and I deserved it. I needed something to persuade me to keep the fight up. Seeing the world alive, vibrant, and bursting with energy made me realize how desperately I wanted to be back in the world, playing golf and hanging out with friends. But at the same time, I understood how much my life had changed. I had swapped golf practice for blood drawing, lunch hours for different medications, study halls for doctors' appointments, and weekend social time for trying to relearn the English language because of my dyslexia-like syndrome. Any other time I was awake, I'd spend talking to *him*, my parents, or my psychologist. At that moment, I understood it was wrong of me to classify myself as a teenager; no, I turned into a professional patient.

42

Christmas day. The smell of snow and happiness floats through the air as a calm silence falls across the city. Silence replaces the sounds of sirens, screams, and the chatter of a typical New York day. The city that never sleeps seems to stand still in time; that is if you don't visit the tree in Rockefeller Center.

Like a young child, I woke up early, excited by the possibility of finding a present from Santa under the tree. We were Jewish, but I never had a Bat-Mitzvah. We always, though, celebrated Christmas. This morning marked the first Christmas my family had spent apart. Christmas did not carry as much meaning as Chanukah, but my mom's absence made the reality of my situation even more damnable. I knew that if it weren't for me, my family would be together. We would snuggle on the couch and watch cheesy Christmas movies while drinking hot cocoa. But no, because of my illness, we were 1,500 miles apart. I carried the weight of dealing with my disease daily, but the guilt I felt from breaking most of my parents' plans weighed heavily on me. This is what life with a chronic illness is like, unpredictability and loneliness. The holiday season used to be my favorite time of year. Years past, I spent Christmas laughing and enjoying the time with my family, but my fate was out of my hands, and I feared it would remain this way.

As I flung back the covers, I scurried into the foyer and saw my present wrapped in sparkling silver wrapping paper with a big red bow on top, sitting angled on the dining table. Feelings of resentment and guilt slowly washed away as I moved toward the glittering box in anticipation, until I turned and saw *him* sitting in the living room chair.

His usual smirk played across his lips, and his clenched fists were visible from his suit pockets. I knew why he showed up so early today. On most days, he wouldn't stop by until late afternoon, but as our relationship furthered and I became weaker, he showed up more frequently and, of course, at the worst possible times. But today he had come because of the irrational decisions I'd made over the past week, and he wanted to "sternly" warn me about the danger ahead. I got the message loud and clear.

"Merry Christmas, Lauren," he said. His smirk became a smile.

"If you're here to reprimand me, I'm not going to take it. I know, I know; I should be more cautious, take my meds on time, and not exert myself too much. But have you ever thought about the situation from my perspective? I'm a teenage girl. I want to experience life as a young, naïve girl should, exploring and rejoicing in all things exciting. For once in these past few months, I wanted to feel life without the restraints of my mysterious illness. Forget listening to my body; I wanted to follow my heart. I wanted to do things spontaneously and experience the adventures that followed. So, yes, I'm in terrible shape today. I've lost seven more pounds, and none of my clothes fit. My hands won't stop trembling, and I've slept for a combined total of 20 hours over the past five days. So sue me. It's my fault, and, yes, I feel like utter crap, but even knowing what is to come, I wouldn't trade these experiences or the laughter I've shared with my dad for the world. So go ahead and yell at me, but I'm not going to feel sorry for myself."

His smile faded away immediately as he slowly got up and moved toward where I stood to lean against the table. As his eyes met mine, he gave me a consoling look and wrapped me in his arms. A soft murmur caught in his throat, and suddenly, I felt a dampness on my forehead. *Oh, my god, he is crying. The man who tried to kill me and torments me is crying in my arms because of what I said.*

"L-L-Lauren?" he managed to say under his breath.

"Yes.."

"I-I-I just came to say that you're my best friend and that however long this takes, I will be here with you throughout everything. You are never alone, and you never will be. I'm always here. Always. I'm sorry for talking to you during your classes in school and during your doctors' appointments, but guilt has lingered inside of me since the day we met about what I've told you, and I just wanted you to feel as if you had someone. If you don't want me, I can go away. But I hope we can continue to be friends."

We were both crying hysterically over this new-found friendship when my dad abruptly walked into the living room.

Half-asleep, he asked, "Who were you talking to?"

Embarrassed by the realization that my dad couldn't see *him*, I quickly said, "Oh, just Mom. She called to wish me a Merry Christmas and told me what she got me."

"Oh, okay, tell her I love her and miss her dearly. I wish she could be with us today."

"Sure thing, Dad; love you."

"Love you, hun," he replied. And with that, he went back into the bedroom to sleep a little while longer, as it was 7:30 am.

I wished my mom could be with us that day, but I also wished my mysterious illness had never existed. But if none of this had ever happened, I wouldn't have met *him*, so maybe everything isn't all that bad after all.

43

As the day progressed, we finally mustered up enough energy to see the tree in Rockefeller Center and the lights along Fifth Avenue. I have never been a big fan of crowds or the loud noises that accompany them, so the excursion was bound to result in a worsening of the symptoms of my debilitating illness. The temperature had warmed up to a balmy 38 degrees. My dad, always cautious, made sure I wore several layers, including a scarf, hat, and gloves, and he made me pack hand warmers in my coat pocket. I did not have a cold or the flu, but my dad somehow thought that extra layering would aid my well-being. I wish my thought processes had allowed me to know enough to bundle up and protect myself from the cold. I had been subjected to illness too profoundly and for far too long to understand self-care. Illness changes you.

The sun began to set as we headed out onto the windy city streets. The activity of life began to pick up as people finished dinner and wandered around aimlessly, enjoying the holiday in all its glory. Although born in New Jersey, I considered the city my second home, as the side streets ran along like the creases in my palms. Put me in small-town America, and I'd be lost, but place me in New York City, and I'd find my way out in a heartbeat. It seemed to help my nerves to know where we were and where we were going, although, as the crowd grew denser, I quickly changed my mind. I grasped my dad's hand tightly as he navigated us through the hordes of people just standing and observing the sights—some walking and some eating. I tried my best to calm myself down from the stimuli overload. I could hear the sound of every breath inhaled and exhaled, every zipper on a coat pocket, every cough, sneeze, or motion. Imagine being able to listen to people's thoughts and actions before they happened and while they were happening. Now multiply that times the number of people out and about in New York City on Christmas who are going to see the tree. My mind couldn't process everything, and my thoughts quickly spiraled out of control like a car on black ice. Soon my vision followed, and, in an instant, all I saw was darkness.

"DAD!" I screamed through the crowds of people, hoping he could hear me as I tugged on his hand.

"WHAT, SWEETHEART?" He turned around, placed his hands on my shoulders, and looked at me searchingly. I couldn't see the look of concern in his eyes as he noticed the worry in mine.

"I CAN'T SEE! EVERYTHING IS BLACK. PITCH BLACK."

I felt him push me along through the crowd with his hands on my shoulders. A few seconds later, he sat me down on a set of stairs before he pulled away and reached in his pocket to grab his phone. When I heard the clacking away of letters on his iMessage keyboard, I realized he was texting my mom.

"L, let's sit here for a minute, ok? You used to get like this when you were a little girl. All the sights, sounds, and smells used to be overwhelming, and you'd shut down. Well, you wouldn't lose your vision, but, you know, you get the point." He dealt better with a crisis with a side of humor or sarcasm; then, he could remain calm. I chuckled lightly at his comment. It was pretty funny, after all. It was as though I were a giant flashlight, and suddenly my batteries drained, and my 'light' stopped working. You couldn't make this up.

Time passed for an extended period before we got up and started for the tree again. I kept my hands by my ears. I imagined lying peacefully on my bed staring up at the ceiling at the glow-in-the-dark star stickers that I so desperately needed to take down from years ago but haven't gotten around to it because they were sentimental and pretty and *for crying out loud I'm almost seventeen I need to grow up*. Off-topic; sorry. I tapped my dad on the shoulder, signaling my readiness to start again, and we ventured out into the streets, still engulfed in darkness.

We made it to the tree but, given my lack of vision, it didn't excite me as I had imagined it would. After asking two obnoxiously loud women to move, my dad placed me directly in front of the tree to get a shot. I smiled and held my eyes open, not knowing where to look until my dad directed me where to point my corneas.

"A little more left. No, sorry; your right. Got it. Good; great, L! Smile. Oh, what a great shot!"

You never really understand how fortunate you are until the privilege given to you is taken away. Although temporary, the sudden blindness reminded me to be more appreciative of the little things. As my health worsened, I had to set the bar low when I would remind myself of all I had to be grateful for each day. I was thankful for the ability to breathe on my own and to wake up to a new day; these things I learned to never take for granted, similar to my eyesight. The world seems so sinister when you are unable to see it. If there is anything I took away from this trip to New York, it was gratitude. Giving prayers of thankfulness became a part of my daily routine. Oh; and if you're reading this, Dad, your photography skills rock:

44

As soon as the landing gear struck the runway, a flood of relief swept over my body. Home, my bedroom, and my life as I had known it before going to New York seemed like such a foreign concept now. Every ounce of me felt drained from my appointment with Dr. P. How could a doctor tell a patient that her symptoms were merely a manifestation of her "tickled imagination" (to quote her exact words), or that they couldn't even happen? All along, I thought doctors were heroes because they solved medical mysteries and saved people's lives. I was wrong (again).

My mom sped around the terminal in her usual fashion, coming to a sudden halt right by the curb where my dad and I stood. I love my mom, but she cannot brake a car delicately to save her life. The tires screeching to a halt brought a smile to my face. I had missed my mom's antics while we were away; I needed the humor she brought to my life. She jumped out of the car, ran around to the passenger's side, and flung the door open with a smile across her face.

"Your chariot awaits, miss," she said.

She reached her hands into the car and took my backpack off my back. Without my family and our sense of humor, this disease would have destroyed the best of me.

* * * * *

Once inside, my dog Charlie greeted me with a broad grin and ferocious tail wag. He flopped onto my lap as I sat on my bed, and I stroked his soft, cloud-like fur. He could tell I was stressed, and he soon started panting in sympathy. Charlie could sense when things were not normal, and now being one of those times. We had moved off the bed and sat on the floor by the edge of my bedroom door, so we could hear my parents arguing in the kitchen. Although Charlie couldn't understand anything, I know he was intrigued, too. *He* soon joined us also; he sat across from us, cross-legged, with extremely dark circles under his eyes. When the shouts turned to murmurs, my inquisitive spirit took over.

"So you pulled an all-nighter, plotting the best way to warn someone else about their impending doom?"

He wasn't in the mood.

"Lauren, the only person I interact with is you. Why do you have to be such a bitch sometimes? You know I'm here to help you; why do you have to go around alienating those who are just trying to make your hellish life a tad easier? What did I ever do to you?"

That came out of nowhere. Wow. *He* saw the hostility and vulnerability in my eyes as I tried to digest his thoughts. He knew the pain he caused, but even now, after everything he had put me through, he didn't seem fazed. Ten minutes ago, I had a best friend who accompanied me to every doctor's appointment, every blood-drawing, every 3 am trip to the bathroom to vomit – and now this?

My words felt emotionless and powerless, so I decided not to retort. I couldn't use sarcasm because no longer was I in the mood, and he did not deserve a comical anecdote from me to ease the tension. No, if he wanted that, he would have to work on resolving this situation himself.

Humans are notorious for spitting words out like fiery nails without conscious thought. Words can make or break a person, and I learned this the hard way. A prime example is my failure to verbalize the truth about my symptoms and what was occurring to me daily. I did not think much of this. I just blamed others' perceptions of me (mostly my parents and teachers) for the reason I had kept quiet. Subconsciously, however, there existed a large part of me that didn't vocalize these thoughts for an entirely different reason. That is to say that the life I am living is actual hell. I hadn't made the connection until the very moment he uttered those words, and I lost it.

45

"Honey? What's the matter? What can we do to help you? We are sorry. We don't mean to upset you with our yelling. Everything will be okay, I promise," my mom hugged me from the side as my back fell against the wall in agony. Her tone, one I had not heard from her before, convinced me that whatever was going on involved me. For once, I was not agonizing in pain; I felt emotionally numb from the realities of my life hitting me smack dab in the face.

I don't remember much of that night, but I do remember waking up, sprawled across my bed like a starfish, and hearing the sound of my parents chatting away again, but this time in a more chipper mood. Given the events of last night, the last thing on my agenda was to make a scene, so I decided to stay in bed and wait. And wait, I did. Two hours later, dying of thirst, I forced myself out of my bedroom to grab some water. As I walked out, I saw my parents huddled in their usual position over the dining room table—the spot they took when they discussed business or critical life decisions.

Considering the only source of "drama" in their lives at the moment was me, I tried to ignore the incredibly awkward silence between the three of us as I quickly went for a glass of water. My skin turned whiter with each passing day, and, in this instance, I hoped this played to my advantage and somehow camouflaged me from the situation. (Silly, I know, but a girl can dream.) I walked as quickly as my brittle legs could back to my bedroom to avoid confrontation when the inevitable happened.

"Hey, sweetie. We need to talk to you." My dad's voice was just barely above a whisper.

Here we go.

"Lauren. We are not mad at you, and you've done absolutely nothing wrong, but your father and I are just concerned about going forward with the pill cam test for several reasons—"

"More like one," my dad interjected slyly.

"Peter. Enough," my mom retorted dryly.

They both paused and stared at each other, then down at the table and then back to me, simultaneously. My parents' emotions escalated as my mom tried to reposition her stance on the topic. I, on the other hand, felt enormous guilt and stress. While waiting for her response, a giant pit opened up in my stomach, and I felt food crawl up my esophagus so quickly I didn't have time to excuse myself before I made a beeline to the bathroom. Between bouts of vomiting, I could hear my parents bickering yet again. I heard a lot of phrases (mostly profanity) but one stuck out in particular:

"There you go, Peter. You made her vomit yet again. Way to go."

I tried to digest this for a moment, better than my body could with food at least before I washed up and headed back out into the living room. Why on earth would my mom think that my dad caused me to throw up? My mom had never used the blame game in arguments with my dad or me. Tonight for the first time, she blamed my dad for my vomiting. But why? There had to be a pretty valid reason why she would pin my illness on my dad, and that's when the lightbulb went off in my mind. She blamed him not for the vomit, but for the sickness itself. My dad has ulcerative colitis, so she probably thinks that whatever I have I inherited from him. Instead of taking the anger out on the mysterious disease, she's pinning the blame on my dad. Wow, what a way of thinking, Mom.

An outfit change later, I entered the "hot seat" in our dining room and waited for my mom to start the conversation a second time. My little "scene" did not help ease the stress of the situation. My parents appeared calmer after I assumed they realized that they were dealing with a sick child and that child being me.

My mom took a large sip of coffee and began, "Lauren, your father and I don't mean to stress you with our fighting, but it is our frustration over the fact that we haven't been able to help you feel better. It seems like it's been months now, and despite each treatment we have tried with you, your condition has grown worse. We do know there is a chance that you have Crohn's because Dr. M and K both said slight ulcerations appeared in the small intestine, but we are concerned that we aren't looking at the full picture. We think that (and this is totally up for debate because it is your body) the best course of action is to agree to do the pill cam, but we have to make a compromise if we do so."

I could see my mom was trying everything in her power not to break down in tears at this moment, and my dad, sensing it, placed his hand on her forearm and stroked her arm. This moment felt frozen in time and had me worried. Compromise on what?

"We can't afford to take you to Dartmouth, honey."

The sentence lingered in the air for seconds before she became unhinged. It hit me pretty hard as well. My mom and I had this trip planned for months. It was my Chanukah present from the year before. We planned on flying to Newark and driving up to see Dartmouth, and on the way back, we would stop to visit some family friends. The thought of not going felt like someone took the air out of my body and replaced it with sludge. I wasn't as upset about the trip as my mom or I had anticipated, but another thought did float across my mind: do these kinds of universities even want me? I hid my growing doubt by starting up the conversation again. My mom, clutching the tissue box, looked up as I began to speak.

"It-It's ok, Mom. We can go another time. I was looking forward to visiting all of the campuses, but, given my condition, it may not be the best time anyway, and maybe when we do go, I'll be in better health."

I needed her to stop crying because if she didn't, I would, and if I cried, she'd feel even more guilt, which is something she did not need. Positivity about the situation had to work, and the statement was accurate: it would be best to visit when my health improved.

"Ok, Mom. Please don't cry; I know we will go another time soon.

"Again, we are so sorry. We thought we could manage, but your father's deal fell through, and we don't have the money. We thought the insurance company would cover most of the costs, like the colonoscopy, but they came back and denied the claim."

"Why would they deny the claim?" I demanded.

"They said it was unnecessary because you had a colonoscopy that came up inconclusive. If something came up on the colonoscopy, the insurance company would cover it. However, they think having the procedure done on you is 'experimental,' so they won't cover a single penny."

"Experimental?? Are you kidding? Nothing about this is experimental, Mom! We're trying to figure out if I have a life-altering, auto-immune disease, not trying to make a lab rat of myself!"

"We know, hon, welcome to health insurance in America."

My dad nodded his head in unison.

"May I ask," I started, with a lump beginning to form in the back of my throat. "How much does the pill camera test cost out of pocket?"

My parents both fell silent. My mom flashed her eyes at my dad. My dad, with the courage of the Joad family in The Grapes of Wrath, whispered the price under his breath so softly that I had to ask him to repeat it.

It was $2,100.

My parents and I decided that this would be the best course of action and that the trip would have to wait. Health takes priority over any college trip. We also decided to appeal the insurance claim because of their outrageous labeling of the procedure as 'experimental.' My parents sent a personal letter on my behalf, explaining why this test was necessary, and they also included a recommendation from Dr. M. They felt confident that the insurance company would rescind their decision, given my prior health record and the doctor's advice. At least, that's what we hoped. Spending this kind of money is not easy for my family, and the guilt started to mount the night before the planned procedure. I knew that there was a good possibility I would regain my good health by going through with it. I felt remorseful, though, spending money my parents didn't have on a test that may or may not yield significant results, and I was scared, too. Would this be another expensive way to figure out that there is nothing wrong with me? At this rate, my parents would go broke within the next year if they kept throwing money into tests like this. My growing uneasiness and regret made me want to believe what the other doctors had said; that "it's a psychological issue" and "it's all in her head." Maybe if I pretended to feel better, I could convince myself that I was indeed getting well. I decided if the test came back negative, I would have to try this route. No other path existed, and no more money to throw into the mysterious black pit of my life.

46

Hungry. I am hungry. I should be used to fasting by now, but I'm not. I roll over and stare at my alarm clock, hoping it's later than it appears to be by the darkness seeping underneath my blinds. 4:37 am. I'm not supposed to go into my gastroenterologist's office until 9:00 am, and food is off-limits until noon. As my stomach roared at the thought of having to wait, I clutched it, hoping to quiet its demands.

"You do realize that wrapping your arm tightly around yourself isn't going to stop your stomach from wanting food, right?"

Although I hadn't mastered fasting, I could recognize this voice immediately. *He* and I had not seen each other in a few days; this being the longest time we had been apart since our first encounter, and I certainly was not in the mood to battle him now.

"What do you want?" I grumbled.

"Ohhh, I guess someone isn't in the mood today," he replied, mimicking the voice of a baby. He seemed to have forgotten about the time he called me a bitch; he wasn't getting off that easily.

"You expect me to act all nicey-nice to you after you went on a rant about how I'm an awful bitchy person?"

"What are you talking about, Lauren? I would never say anything like that to you."

"Quit the act. Now is not the time to use sarcasm; seriously. I have not been myself after our conversation, and it made me upset."

"Seriously, Lauren, I am not joking with you. I never uttered any of those words."

His tone reached a depth I had not heard him use before, leading me to question my claim. I swear I heard him utter those words, but it did seem out of character for him to do so. Did I dream about him saying those words, or was it indeed reality? Or maybe he did talk to me like that, and he's excellent at lying…

FUTURE LAUREN:

No, Lauren, it's neither of those excuses. It's because your central nervous system (CNS) is under attack, causing your life to be an entirely false façade that you thoroughly believe to be true. But sure, you're just fine.

47

When I arrived at my gastroenterologist's office, a wave of nervousness came over me, and my thoughts began to spiral; the peripheral "what if?" stayed centered in my mind. *What if this test shows nothing? What if I just wasted a lot of my parents' money? What if I do have cancer? What if they do find something that confirms that all of these symptoms are real?* The last thought, more than any, caused my skin to crawl. I wished severely for my ailments to be a bad dream. I would wake up, and my life would be normal. But what if this state of being is my new "normal"? I had to face my destiny, whatever that may be.

When the nurse led my mom and me back to the exam room, she had my mom fill out some last-minute release forms, which I then had to initial, confirming my release. I should have listened to my mom about not reading the fine print of medical contracts but, of course, being a teenager. I didn't.

"May cause death?! Mom, are you sure I should do this?" I exclaimed anxiously, breathing heavily.

"Hun, you'll be fine. You only have to swallow the pill and excrete it. Now, if you can't swallow the pill and it gets lodged into your esophagus, then there are several doctors here to help you. But you can do this, so let's get this over with, ok?"

We were both on edge. Every test or lab report felt as if we might have the winning "ticket," the one that would unlock the "prize" of good health and return my family to a state of homeostasis. Yet, after eight months, the idea of a "ticket" seemed like an anomaly.

I begrudgingly agreed, and the nurse strapped the equipment onto my upper body. I would have to wear it for six hours. The unit strapped around my waist like an ugly fanny pack and contained a mini-computer. The computer would store all of the photos taken over the course of the six hours. When she said I could click on the home button to see what the photos of my intestines looked like, my mother cringed and banned me from showing her the images. Of course, I still intended to show her! She then instructed me as to when I could eat again and gave me more specific information about the test, such as that by 6:00 pm, the camera will have taken over 57,000 photos of my insides. The aspiring physician inside of me squirmed in excitement about the real-life anatomy I'd get to learn, and with none other than myself as the subject!

The day shaped up to be semi-decent, considering it fell under "procedure day" on the family calendar. My mom knew that any date on the calendar with those words written down was depressing for me. My mom would get me a small gift, and I'd find it by my bed when I woke up to brighten up the day. You rock, Mom.

He seemed to be in good spirits too. After our little hiccup earlier, we forgave each other and moved on to prepping for the procedure. For the first time since I had known him, he smiled sincerely at me when the nurse strapped-on my belt monitor. That alone made me feel confident that going through with this was indeed the right choice. Besides, he knew more about my illness than I did, so if he smiled, I should smile, right? Taking after his lead, I smiled for the photo my mom took of me displaying my new outfit, as he wrapped his arms around my shoulder. Seeing him smile made me smile too. I began to have an unknowing awareness that somehow everything would turn out all right.

Are you wondering where he is? He is standing right beside me with his arm looped through mine. Pretty obvious, I thought. I mean there's no other guy in the photo with a tuxedo on, is there?

48

The next day, after I had to return my trendy fashion accessory, I woke up early to study for my AP Biology exam. I couldn't for the life of me spell *apoptosis*. I used sandpaper, traced each letter at least five times, and sounded out the word with help from my phonics book, but it just wasn't sticking. Feelings of inadequacy began to boil inside of me because I wasn't able to spell a simple word. I could spell *monounsaturated fat, polymer, metabolism,* and *entropy* with no problem, but when it came to *apoptosis,* I had no clue. I walked away from my desk and went out to our living room to see what my parents were doing. It was 5:00 am, and they were sleeping but clouded by delusion, I thought they'd be up and about.

I happened to be right that morning. My mom stood bent over the counter, trying to adjust something on the coffee machine. Fidgeting with the handle and trying to force the lid to stay on the coffee carafe, her tension was evident from my vantage point across the room. I would have interrupted her to assist, but then I realized I'd be of little help, so I decided to stay put. I don't remember what made me stay there watching my mom that morning, but I'm glad I did. She kept pursuing different ways to place the carafe back into the coffee maker with no luck; she took it out, and, with one quick shove, she tried to jam it into place. Suddenly, she let out a high-pitched shriek.

"WHY, GOD, DOES IT HAVE TO BE US? WHY US, GOD? WHY?"

The ferocious tone of her voice made my entire body jerk in fright. I had never seen my mother express her emotions with such power and vulnerability before, and, at that moment, the façade broke. It's hard to realize as a teenager that your parents don't have all the answers to life's problems, but, in my case, it was hard to watch my mother, whom I'd never seen cry before, scream like that over me.

49

He followed me into my classroom and pulled the seat behind me closer, so he was a hand's length away from my ear. It seemed unusual, given that he usually sat right next to me, but maybe he wanted a change of scenery, so he decided to switch spots. He was harder to read than *Hamlet* without subtext. I grabbed my pencil case from my backpack and took out a pencil, careful not to pull out my phonics book and sandpaper, too, because that would result in never-ending embarrassment. As our teacher began to hand out the test, the room fell silent. Unusual for a class of only six people, but given that this test was the going to be the hardest of the year, with fifty multiple-choice and six short answers, everyone's nerves were on high alert. The teacher placed the test pamphlet on my desk. I flipped open the front page and stared at all the questions. They were nothing but a jumble of letters, but, then again, that's how everything I read looked to me.

I would spend the first few minutes translating the test into English, so it wasn't just a random assortment of letters on a page. I traced the letters and silently sounded out the vowels to recall how to spell a word or phrase like *cytoplasm* or *endoplasmic reticulum*. I would rewrite each question and each answer choice in English, and, one by one, I would try to answer the questions. You may be wondering why I didn't translate the entire test before starting, and that is because it would be a waste of time. Once I rewrote it, it didn't make it correct. No, it looked even worse, a sort of semi Mandarin-Spanglish language that I never knew existed. My tactic worked if I didn't have a time limit, which rarely occurred.

Halfway through the multiple-choice questions, I heard him start tapping his fingers on his desk. I turned around and flashed him an angry look, signaling him to stop. He raised his eyebrows in surprise, stopped for a moment, then began to tap away again.

"Seriously, I need to focus. Please stop," I whispered under my breath.

"Nah, I'm bored. You didn't tell me that this class period would involve silence; otherwise, I wouldn't have joined you."

"Well, if you're so disappointed, why don't you just leave now?" I tried to keep my annoyance in check as I continued to translate questions.

"Well, with that attitude, I certainly won't. I need to be there for you, Lauren. Especially on a day like today."

Confused, I turned and faced him. "What's that supposed to mean?"

"Oh, well, you know, test days are difficult for you, so I want to be your moral support! Woot! Gooooo, Lauren!!"

I turned back around, continuing to unscramble the messiness of an AP Biology short answer question.

"Seriously, stop. I don't want the others to hear you."

"Lauren, don't worry about them. Anyway, this conversation is boring me. So did you hear the latest about gas prices?"

It took all my might not to allow my rage get the best of me because I soon remembered what occurred when my emotions did get the best of me. I decided to shut my mouth and do the best I could on my exam. I had three questions left.

"Hello? Earth to Lauren. Answer my question."

"What? No, of course, I have not heard about gas prices. Why would you ask me such a thing? I don't even have my license yet!"

"Well, that's an even better reason for you to listen and learn! Gas prices vary depending on the season. You must investigate to get the best price per gallon from these gas stations. The location of the station and the different grades of fuel will vary greatly in price. It gets a little grey in this area for me, but you can figure out which gas stations offer the best price, and then you can save money!"

I tried to hide my laughter as hiccups.

"I don't even drive, and I know that you should do your research before you fill up at a gas station," I could barely say with a straight face.

"Oh, well, look at you, miss smarty pants. Some of us don't have the luxury of knowing the gas price bargain hunt."

I turned around to him and flashed him a quick smile before I realized I had five minutes before the fourth-period bell would ring. Amazingly, I made it to the last question, and I just needed to unscramble the previous sentence and answer it quickly, to the best of my knowledge. As I unscrambled that sentence, he started to sing. Of course, I wouldn't expect anything else from him. He put on quite a performance today, gas prices and all. It was exhausting, forcing my brain to focus on the page instead of the cacophony inside my head. The exercise was enough to make me want to sleep for days.

The bell rang, and I slid my pencil away as my teacher came around to collect our tests. I felt pretty confident, and I would feel more so if he would've just shut up, but I could never ask for that. We both got up and pushed in our chairs as he followed me out the door and down the hall to my Precalculus class. He sat next to me for every test and quiz, just rambling on about the most random of subjects, while I tried my best to unscramble questions. Gas prices, monopoly, and birch trees were just some of the more intriguing conversations he started. I soon learned to focus my attention between him and the test or quiz in front of me. To this day, I can leave the windows open in my bedroom and be unfazed by the rushing traffic outside. I guess I can thank him for that.

50

We got our tests back a week later, and I surprisingly scored the highest in my class with an 89% overall on both the multiple-choice section and free-response. I asked my teacher if he gave me the wrong test back, but he looked at me with a confused expression.

"Of course, Lauren. This is your test.."

I swear, to this day, I still do not know how I managed to perform as well as I did in school.

The day had finally arrived. Slipping out of my bed cautiously, as if the floor beneath me were glass, I tiptoed to my bathroom to get ready for the momentous day. Seven months of waiting had led up to this day. Every day I was consumed with symptoms different from the day before. Each day my prayers for relief were once again unanswered. Within nine hours, I'd be a different person, a healthy person. I would no longer need to suppress having to vomit or suffer the nauseating headaches that would arise out of nowhere. I could enjoy the ability to eat more than one piece of solid food per day and be able to read without the letters switching order on me. I would no longer suffer the inescapable dizziness every evening, or lie in bed with pains that felt as if someone had taken a butcher knife to each vertebra. I'd finally be healthy, or at least closer to it.

My dad decided to take the day off from work to join us at Dr. M's office. I wanted to feel relief that both of my parents would be at my life-altering appointment, but I didn't. My dad coming with us solidified the reality I had been afraid to face all along: I was genuinely sick. My father's presence meant that the news was going to be catastrophic, not just for me, but for my family as a whole. From this day forward, the way we lived our lives would change because of my illness, which would now have a name.

The weight of the day started to sink in as we drove in silence down I-75. From our condo to Dr. M's office, it took around twenty minutes, but the silence between my mom, my dad, and I seemed to make the ride much longer and more uncomfortable. It began to dawn on me that I would never be a typical girl because of this disease. My life would revolve around medications and doctors' appointments. I wouldn't be able to go on dates to a restaurant without fear that they may cross-contaminate my food and end up causing me more grief. I wouldn't be able to stay in a dorm in college for fear of exposing my suppressed immune system to other illnesses. I wouldn't be able to do the usual things that most teens and twenty-somethings get to experience (like traveling abroad). Within the span of that twenty-minute drive, the dreams I had for my future flew out the window.

51

"Lauren Kingsly?"

"Here," my parents and I said in unison.

I stood up first and paused, waiting for my parents to go ahead of me. I knew I needed to face this head-on, but I needed my parents to protect me from reality, one last time. There was too much to process and too little time to absorb the information. As my parents looked at me in confusion, my dad motioned for my mom to go first, and he followed behind me soon after.

He came too, and as I went to follow my parents down the corridor to Dr. M's office, he grabbed my wrist. As always, he sported his three-piece tuxedo, but his black dress shoes seemed brighter than usual. Maybe he had polished them for this "momentous" day.

"Lauren," he cautioned me.

I snapped, not wanting to hear this tone from him today. "What?"

"Today won't solve anything. It only brings you closer to the end," he said solemnly.

"Seriously? You're going there today? Today of all days—the day I might finally have a chance to turn my life around and live instead of being sick—you're telling me not to get my damned hopes up? I thought we were in this together. What happened to that?"

He looked around, trying to gauge how those around us were receiving my outburst. Not well, I assumed from his reaction. Grabbing me by the arm, he dragged me along through the long corridor, and into the viewing room Dr. M had set up for us to look at the photographs collected from the pill cam test. He shoved me into the first chair, and I tried not to hear the word as it fell from Dr. M's mouth:

"Inconclusive."

"What does this mean?" my parents asked, again in unison.

Dr. M tried to reposition her stance and gather the courage to break the news to my parents that their daughter was still an unlabeled mystery.

"From the pictures we gathered, she does have some ulcerations in her small intestine and ilium that we were unable to get in the colonoscopy, but they are so small that they should not be giving her the list of symptoms she is describing. Going by the medical textbook, she has Crohn's disease, but I don't think it's the full story."

"Wait; you just said it was inconclusive, and now you're saying she has Crohn's?" Annoyance was evident in my father's tone.

"Yes, she does have the beginnings of what Crohn's disease looks like, but there is still more investigating to do. Given every symptom she has and everything she is going through, I do not think these ulcerations are the cause of her misery. I know they are not helping, but I don't think they are the full story."

My parents and I relaxed as we listened to Dr. M continue reviewing the results of the pill cam test. Although the results were not what any of us wanted, at least we had one puzzle piece to add to the blurry picture that was my health. My dad started to relax once he heard what Dr. M had to say, and the entire time I thanked God for having these ulcerations show up. It sounds terrible, I know, but at that point, I wanted an answer. I wanted something tangible that I could point to as the likely source of my madness. At the moment, these tiny ulcerations dotting my small intestine seemed to be it.

Dr. M then spoke about the different classifications of mesalamine drugs. These drugs are used to treat Ulcerative Colitis and Crohn's. I tried to pay attention as she listed the positive and negative side effects of each drug, but my mind couldn't follow. As I stared blankly into Dr. M's eyes, all I could hear were *his* words: "It only brings you closer to the end."

In the end, she prescribed Pentasa, believing that it would help with the majority of my gastrointestinal issues. I had to take two pills four times a day. Pills were already a staple of my daily routine, so adding another eight didn't faze me.

We walked out of the appointment with less hope than we had anticipated but still more than usual. *He* grabbed my hand from behind me and squeezed it with a solemn look in his eye. I knew he was sorry, and that he had just wanted to tell me what to expect. I appreciated that, but I wished that for once, he was wrong.

As we all piled back into my dad's SUV and drove to CVS to get my first Pentasa prescription, my parents looked at each other with dread in their eyes. My mom and I stayed in the car while my dad went into the pharmacy. *He* remained in the car with us, too. Neither he nor I uttered a single word. When my dad returned, he handed me the bulky prescription bag, and I carefully tore open the packaging as my mom gave me a bottle of water.

Placing two abnormally large pills into my mouth, I took a large sip of water and swallowed. *Here goes nothing*, I thought.

PART THREE

"The trouble is,
you think you have time."

– Buddha

52

Perspiration soaked my bedsheets as I thrashed around, trying to find a comfortable position to ease my dizziness. My legs, numb to the touch, were unable to help move my body, making the process of finding relief even more daunting. The dark ceiling fan above my bed appeared to be moving closer to my head. With each turn of the blades, I tried to slide myself, using only my upper body strength, out of the way. With impending doom lurking, my anxiety and blood pressure steadily rose, as I remained stuck in a vulnerable position. The only part of my body that wasn't numb was my trunk. My head lay drenched in sweat on the pillow. Due to some unseen force beyond my control, I was unable to move it. Sharp pains shot through my legs, leaving them immobile. It felt as if someone had taken a power drill and began drilling holes through my shins while simultaneously duct-taping my mouth and head to the bed to keep still. The powerlessness of the situation only fueled my anxiety further, and I screamed out in terror for *him* or someone to help me. My eyes darted back and forth between the lowering fan blades and my bedroom door as I hoped that someone would come to save me, but this only made it worse.

Covered in sweat, I squirmed as I tried relentlessly to move my body to the edge of my bed by sheer willpower. Inch by inch, I scooted until I sensed the leveling off of my mattress. The fan blade merely hovered over my head. There was no turning back. I began to weigh the options of my fate: to be beheaded by a fan blade or fall an uncertain depth to possible harm. The second seemed preferable, so I shifted my body weight to the edge of my mattress as sweat continued to pour out of every pore.

Immobility struck my entire body; slowly at first, but then all at once. As I fell, my legs and arms began jerking rapidly, and my mouth salivated furiously. I remember blinking uncontrollably, and, as the room turned black, I prayed for relief, wishing God would take me to heaven.

Hours later, I realized that God had *not* answered my prayers (yet again) as I woke feeling, of all things, refreshed. I do not recall the remainder of the evening, but when I had managed to sit up, I saw my mom passed out on my bed beside me, clutching a pillow with all her might. The veins in her forehead were visible and streaked with purple marks as she bit her lip in frustration. She seemed in no position to be awakened, so I left her and walked to my bathroom, as school began soon.

When I had looked at the clock earlier, it was 3:30 am. It was currently 6:51 am. That means I had slept for three hours and 21 minutes—a new record.

I had not yet regained full feeling in my left arm. It was challenging for me to put my hair into a ponytail using only my right arm. Soon, I brushed my teeth, swallowed my assortment of useless pills, and ate a few raspberries without any ill effect. I considered this to be a successful morning.

I hoped that today would be different, because it was the day of my AP Biology exam. My mom and I knew that I would not be strong enough to endure a three-hour exam. Before the testing date, we had emailed the proctor to schedule a make-up exam. Unfortunately, we found out the make-up exam would only be offered on the day I had to be in Tampa for overnight observation. There was no alternative; the College Board wouldn't process any special requests. Make-up exams were only allowed on the specified days. Today was my only opportunity to take my AP Biology exam, so I had to take it.

We did not have enough time to file for additional accommodations after my diagnosis of Crohn's disease. I was allowed timed breaks. I adopted the "something is better than nothing" attitude because I could at least stop the clock, and being negative about the situation would only make matters worse. I walked into the testing room with a semi-clear head and positive mental state when my stomach began to feel off.

The nauseous feeling I knew all too well started up again as the glaring overhead lights made my skin burn. The proctor began to read the directions and rules about the exam, but her words were inaudible as my heartbeat began to beat louder and louder within my ears. I flashed *him* a look of desperation as he sat there in the corner next to me, but he didn't respond. For once, he was at a loss for words. I began to worry. The numbness started to crawl up my legs until I could barely feel my lower extremities, but also because of his expression; I had never seen him quite like that. A mixture of sorrow, helplessness, despair, and panic filled his features, and I couldn't help but freak out even more. The proctor motioned for me to open my test booklet and begin; diagrams and random symbols sprawled over each page as I scanned for room to rewrite the questions. With a trembling hand, I moved my pencil over the letters and retraced them to figure out what they were trying to spell.

M. I lost vision in my left eye. *I.* He started to speak Portuguese to me. *C.* A wave of dizziness came over me. *R.* I lost my spot on the page as the walls inched closer to me with every tick of the second hand on the clock. *O.* Pulsating pain in my spine began. *B.* I needed to go to the restroom badly—very badly. *I.*

Food inched further up my esophagus toward my mouth. *O.* I told my proctor I needed to use the restroom as I ran out of the testing room in a panic. *M.* Locking myself in a stall, I trembled violently as I vomited. *E.* Forty-five minutes later, I re-entered the testing room with another teacher who found me curled on the floor in a fetal position. I had ten minutes left, and all I had done was unscramble the word *microbiome.*

PART FOUR
TWO MONTHS LATER

"The ability to delude yourself may be
an important survival tool."

– Jane Wagner

53

The sun began to set along the horizon as my boyfriend and I headed back from our excursion to see the Lava River Cave. (Yes, I had a boyfriend!) *He* came along, too, wearing his usual tuxedo. *He* nearly brought me to the edge of a mental breakdown as my boyfriend and I descended inside the dark, cold cave. We spent the day exploring the area around the cave and the breathtaking views they held, but the entire time, my mind was focused elsewhere.

As always, I had bit off more than I could chew. By now, my bones felt as if they were fusing in place. I didn't know how much more my body could take of my abuse, ignoring the undeniable fact that something much bigger was wrong. When they first began, the symptoms were alarming as all hell; but as time went on and tests kept coming back negative, it seemed the only remaining option for me was to accept this state as my new life. Countless prescriptions to manage pain and anxiety that barely managed them, at best, along with a laundry list of dietary restrictions, were just the tip of the iceberg.

If my boyfriend and I weren't together, there would have been a cane in my hand so I could semi-navigate the jolting bone-on-bone pain radiating from my knees and ankles as I moved.

Given my bill of health, it may seem ignorant that I flew halfway across the country to hang out with my boyfriend for the week, but my parents and I viewed this trip in a much more somber light. Each passing day brought more inexplicable symptoms that I couldn't control. One day I would experience severe dizziness to the point of fainting, and the next would bring joint pain so severe I couldn't lift myself out of bed without my mom's help. To my parents, this trip allowed the youth in my body, trapped by illness, to be released. They wanted me to have something to look forward to besides a day here or there on which only a handful of things bothered me; they wanted me to feel alive. I, on the other hand, had a much more morbid take on things. I saw this as an opportunity to try to have some fun like a typical teenager. But the underlying belief was that it would be my last trip, not for the next few years, but the remainder of my years left.

I recognized all the signs. I had now been to a total of nine different doctors all across the state of Florida who all said the same thing phrased nine different ways: *I don't know what's wrong; she seems healthy to me.* I was *the picture of health*, as one doctor in Tampa put it, but that was far from the truth. It felt as if my words rang hollow as I sat drenched in sweat with a low to high-grade fever in each examination room.

"You're a Jersey girl; you're just not used to the Floridian heat!"

"Are you sure you are drinking enough electrolytes? A deficiency of electrolytes and proper minerals can cause hallucinations."

"Take some cold medicine. It seems like a run-of-the-mill cold to me. Should be good to go in three to five days max!"

But I was accustomed to the heat, I took three electrolyte tablets every day, and I tried cold medicine for a week only to have my joint pain escalate to the point of not being able to get off of the toilet myself. No doctor and no test had yet given any indication of any illness, but again nothing ever seemed correct. I knew my body would eventually not be able to withstand the trauma it had gone through and would shut down. As for when I couldn't tell you, but I knew for certain I had to go on this trip before it happened.

My boyfriend and I pulled into the driveway of his parents' ranch house, settled in the lazy mountains of a small Oregonian town. I observed the setting sun in the distance, wishing that just maybe it would happen here. My parents would not have to see me, and the mountains provided a feeling of security that I never felt back in Florida. What I am poorly trying to describe is being *grounded,* and the feeling provided me with the closure that I so desperately needed within myself. I had been fighting the fight for almost a year without any resolve, just praying to see the next day, and I finally felt ok. Ok with not seeing tomorrow or even what the future had in store for my boyfriend and me. Regardless, everything would end up in flames; he'd continue with his pre-determined path in life as mine ended up in the clouds.

For the first time, I felt at peace with the fact that I was indeed dying. That immediately brought a tear to my eye and, surprisingly, a hug from the tuxedo-wearing man I had grown to call my best friend. I turned aside and told my boyfriend I wanted to admire the view a little longer, as a way to hide my emotions. The man flung his arm around my neck as I mechanically turned in my seat, and we both sat watching the sunset together. Hours could have passed for all I know, but my boyfriend remained there in silence as I sat gazing out at the beautiful horizon. As the final rays of sunshine made their descent over the snow-covered mountains, the man leaned in and whispered, "It's okay to give in; no one gets out alive. But you have to understand and listen to me carefully, ok?"

I gave a slight nod to assure him.

"Don't ever let the sun go down on you, you hear me? You may be dying, but this isn't your time. I need you to bring out the fight still left in you. I know it feels as if every ounce of strength has deserted you, but I know you have it. You can and will do this. If you take in anything from what I've just said, know this: you are sick, and you feel like you are dying, but it is not your time. The sun has not set on your show."

His words floated in my mind. The sun disappeared, and so did my desire to die at that moment. I heard the man – it wasn't my time.

54

Depression clouded my mood. However, I tried not to let it affect my time with my boyfriend during that week. I laughed when I felt like crying and screamed with joy when I felt like dying. He may not have understood everything about my illness, but he did a damned good job caring for me. He bought a fan for my room, so when my fevers struck, I'd have some defense besides the air conditioner. He helped me sort out my pills for the day and mapped out the locations of all the different bathrooms at our stops. It was in those moments that I wondered what made a nineteen-year-old guy like him want to be with a girl who was purely dependent on bathrooms and pills. I still don't understand it to this day, but I will forever be grateful to have met him.

Life with him seemed peachy-keen; well, except for one small issue. I first noticed it the second time he kissed me, with his saliva burning as it fell upon my lips and the sudden urge to collapse. I assumed teenage hormones to be the guilty culprits, but I knew better. It was an instantaneous expression, as though my body was disgusted by the idea of being kissed. One day I would feel nauseous, and the next day my lips would break out in hives. The following day, I'd have to break away to run and vomit in the bathroom while trying to blame it on too much sun exposure.

He always told me to be open with how I was doing, a characteristic I always loved about him from the start of our relationship. But I knew that as soon as he heard this, it would be over. I knew he'd be like the rest, believing I had been manipulated by "Jedi mind tricks" that were playing with my emotions. It wasn't normal. How could I explain to my boyfriend of almost six months that he couldn't kiss me because each time he did, the illness inside my body destroyed another small piece of me? I couldn't. At that moment, I knew that our relationship and any relationship I had going forward would be doomed

PART FIVE
SIX MONTHS LATER

"You must not lose faith in humanity. Humanity is an ocean; if a few drops of the ocean are dirty, the ocean does not become dirty."

– Mahatma Gandhi

55

Light is something most take for granted. We rise with it and fall asleep in its absence. In the winter, we wish for its appearance to last longer, while in the summer, we ask for it to make a reprieve. It can be avoidable and unseen, but, eventually, it comes back and peeks its head out to let us know we are all still alive.

Not for me, however. The last six months have proved to be more difficult by the hour as my body continues its vicious revolt. The latest phenomenon is light or the hatred of it. Any exposure to cell phones or TVs and sunlight, in particular, causes insatiable migraines more wicked than can be explained in words; I stand defenseless and undynamic in their force. I've come to appreciate the darkness, but I wish to see the shadows of palm trees swaying in the breeze and the way the water sparkles with excitement during the day. For all I know, the outside world is nonexistent, and these visuals that I once took for granted are gone. Images like these circulate through my mind when I am awake for a mere six hours a day. The ability to function like a normal person has all but vanished, and I rely solely on charades to ask my parents for help. I understand what they are saying, but the words won't slip off my tongue. Instead, a jumble of moans and groans are the only audible sounds I can formulate, and with each passing day, another skill vanishes.

Today is finally the day we have been waiting for, the metaphorical and, hopefully, the literal light at the end of this long, cavernous tunnel that is my health. We are driving to Miami to see a world-renowned gastroenterologist to get a definitive answer on my Crohn's disease. She attended UCLA medical school, did her internship at Brigham Women's Hospital, and has published seven books on the matter, so I felt confident that I could place my faith in her expertise. I knew none of this until my parents started talking during the drive and, being that listening was the only option I had to keep myself distracted from the mind-numbing pain, I paid very close attention. For all my parents knew, I was asleep, since I had to wear my blackout eye mask. Pillows galore supported my every joint as I lay down in the backseat. Ordinarily, they would be right about my being asleep, but the little morsel of energy I had inside me that day told me to remain conscious, for I needed to hear the sound of my parents' voices. I knew that, even if I did get an answer today, the possibility of my not making it remained high. I wanted to remember everything about them, but since my visual impairment began a while ago, I relied on my parents' voices to try to soothe my pain. I made it a priority to listen, even when the sea of sleep called my body, and I faded in and out of conscious awareness, catching only snippets of my parents' conversation. Having no concept of time, I assumed it to be several hours later when our car came to an abrupt halt, jarring me out of my somber sleep. I was only somewhat aware that we had arrived at the hospital. I remained still until the last moment, cautious of the fact that my parents had not spoken a single word in over sixty seconds.

Today, I don't remember that day or the car ride or much of the appointment for that matter, but I do remember my mom's voice, low and cracking, repeating over and over: "Please, dear God, may this woman keep my daughter alive."

56

We waited for three hours—*three long hours*—to see this specialist. Finally, she waved, signaling my parents to bring me back to her consultation room. She had a resident with her who, by his tone, seemed much friendlier and empathetic than her. After my mother spilled my entire medical history for what felt like the thousandth time, she paused a little too long before speaking. What came out of her mouth next is almost too traumatizing for me to write. She degraded me, telling me that I was fabricating my symptoms and that it was impossible for them to be associated with Crohn's. She told me to take my eye mask off. I refused because I assumed there were bright lights in the office, and that only caused her to question my case more and to ask my parents if they had ever considered a psychological hospital instead. Furious, my mom began a tirade. She told the doctor that my symptoms were, indeed, valid and that she had no right to decide otherwise. My mom reminded her that she didn't live with me twenty-four/seven. After my mom's lengthy verbal assault, the doctor finally calmed down, and it appeared she had stopped criticizing me, only to say: "Well, you do have some slight Crohn's, but that is not all that is wrong with you. Given your bizarre symptoms, maybe you have a disease that is too advanced for current westernized medicine. You may be like this for the rest of your life unless a doctor makes a miraculous discovery of a disease that matches your exact symptoms, but until then, I don't think anyone can do anything for you, so you need to accept your new normal." *New normal?* A renowned specialist told my family to accept my "new normal". I knew at that moment my fate was sealed: this will be my life.

Did she think that I had magically slipped into a neurologically comatose state only to be permanently stuck there forever? I knew there had to be an answer. I had wished and prayed to leave the world peacefully in my sleep, but, at this moment, the universe gave me strength to continue and fight, for I wanted nothing in this world but for this doctor to be dead wrong. Tears began to stain the inside of my mask as anger bubbled up inside of me, and I couldn't take it anymore. With newfound strength, I prayed my vocal cords wouldn't fail me as I screamed: "I HATE HER!"

Then, as it had happened all too often, my world went black.

57

ONE MONTH LATER.

"You take A to L, and I'll take M through Z."

After Miami, my family and I realized we needed to take matters into our own hands if we wanted definitive answers. We knew two things: I was chronically ill, and the other was that the doctor's opinions were wrong. I will not live like this forever, and there will be a light at the end of the tunnel. It may be an even more daunting journey than this one, but a path existed—at least my parents thought so. Part of me had hope, but the other part of me firmly believed I was a lost cause. We had seen over a dozen medical professionals, and all of them reiterated the same words: "She's fine." Maybe the universe had dealt my cards, and I needed to deal with my hand. I was okay with giving up; it had been two years, and my desire to continue waned with each passing hour. My parents, on the other hand, were determined to fight for the truth.

My mom decided for her and my dad to scan the alphabet for all possible autoimmune/infectious diseases and play "connect the symptoms". They would further investigate the diseases or disorders with the most matched symptoms and find a specialist. At least with this option, we could narrow down possible explanations without me having to submit more blood and without my parents having to spend more money. I vividly remember lying on the couch drifting off to the sound of the repetitive clicks of a computer mouse as both my mom and dad searched disease after disease on their laptop. There seemed to be no end in sight.

Floating in and out of consciousness, I suddenly thought about my elementary school friend, Madison. Although she was a year younger than me, we were close and spent time exploring her backyard. I recalled that her mom, Cara, had suffered from a debilitating disease, leaving her unable to walk, speak, or even function for days. I remember Cara talking about how doctors seemed to belittle her symptoms, and that she had never really felt healthy since being diagnosed. Each day was a struggle, and sometimes she would be so exhausted that she'd sleep for almost sixteen hours a day to feel semi-functional. Her symptoms seemed to be a match to most of mine, but I couldn't for the life of me think of what her illness was called—that is until I saw a little bug crawl across the coffee table in my living room. It was Lyme disease.

The phrase "Oh. My. God." seemed to be repeated an infinite number of times before it finally reconciled in my ill brain. My parents huddled over my mom's desktop, stood with their mouths agape at the words splayed in front of them on the screen. I stood solemnly and gazed at my parents, trying to say, "What are you looking at?" but with each attempt, my brain fell short, so I waited and hoped they'd notice me. My dad suddenly flashed his eyes in my direction with the sort of terror associated with one of my manic episodes. Seeing my calm state, though, he relaxed and came over to help me walk to the office. I couldn't read anything on the screen, so my mom explained to me that when she searched "Lyme disease", every single symptom I had been experiencing matched.

"Every one?" I asked, doubtful that there could be an explanation for my reality.

"Yes. Here, I'll read them out loud. Chronic exhaustion, severe muscle, and joint inflammation, partial paralysis of the face (Bell's palsy), shivers and shakes, high fevers, neurological issues, brain fog, diarrhea, vomiting, sensitivity to sound and light, lightheadedness, hair loss. Lauren, it is everything you have been through for the past two years."

At that moment, it occurred to me that for the first time in over two years, there actually may be an answer to my "bizarre" symptoms. More importantly, my symptoms weren't conjured up in my head.

My mom called Cara the following morning and reiterated my entire medical history. After she finished, convinced that she had struck gold and found the elusive answer to end my pain and suffering, Cara recommended three different physicians, all of whom practiced the integrative approach to medicine rather than western medicine. That seemed odd, but at this point, considering my delicate balancing act with death, my parents were willing to try anything and everything.

In the meantime, my dad researched Lyme Disease, too. He found a book called "How Can I Get Better?" by Richard Horowitz and began reading it as if it were the Torah. My dad discovered that Dr. Horowitz was a "Lyme Guru" and had helped thousands of people in my condition achieve remission. Dr. Horowitz's patients had gone on to live happy, prosperous lives. My dad became adamant that I visit a physician that acknowledged his work or followed his protocol, ensuring I'd receive the correct treatment.

Things were looking up until my mom discovered that two out of the three physicians were no longer seeing patients. My parents' hearts sank with desperation again. Until recently, I had no idea this had occurred, as my parents hid this bit of information from me. That was probably best, in the interest of saving my life. Only one doctor remained and, ironically, located five miles away from my childhood home in New Jersey. My mom, with dwindling hope and high anxiety, scanned and faxed over the two three-ring binders containing my medical history from the past two years. All our eggs were in this basket; there was no backup or alternative route insight.

My mom's cell phone rang thirty minutes later.

58

"Hi, Christy; this is Jane Duggin from The Gedroic Medical Institute. Your daughter, Lauren…is she the Lauren Kingsly from The Red Oaks School?"

"Yes, she is. Why do you ask?"

"I'm Samantha and Layla's mom. My daughters also attended The Red Oaks School. "

"OMG! Jane, what a small world, thank you for returning my call."

"I saw Lauren's name on the incoming patient email and had to reach out. As of now, our first available appointment for new patients is August 27th, but let me speak with the doctor and see if we can get your daughter in sooner.

"August 27th? Jane, I don't believe Lauren will make it until then. Please, say or do whatever you can, express to the doctor just how dire our daughter's health is.

"I will. Hang in there."

"I will. Thank you."

"Bye."

"Goodbye."

That phone call took place on February 25th. Even I knew I wouldn't make it to August but, unlike the other times, I had waited to see additional specialists. A tiny spark of emotion ignited inside of me that hadn't previously been there in over a year: hope.

Two days later, my mom received another call from Jane at The Gedroic Medical Institute. Someone had canceled their ap-pointment on   March 14ᵗʰ,   and   she   was wondering if we could make the trip to see Dr. Gedroic at 7:30 am that morning. My   mom   said,   "Already booked the flights. We   will   be there." Two weeks later, I took off on a plane headed to New Jersey.

Growing up, I never really believed or understood the concept of fate, God, or guardian angels. I placed my faith in tangible things and thought nothing of these spiritual beings. Funny how faith changes when faith is the only thing you have left.

I experienced a lot of mixed emotions during our travel to New Jersey. The first was that there was still the possibility that Dr. Gedroic may not have any answers for my condition and that this would, indeed, be my new normal. I refused to believe it, though. My mindset was akin to a child in a candy store. "I want it, and I need it." Anything beyond the realm of simple tasks like saying "Hello" or stating my name for the TSA agent at the gate seemed too daunting to handle.

The second emotion I experienced was happiness. Maybe af-ter all this time we would receive an answer, and I'd be given a magic pill to cure me of all maladies. Given my state of health at the time, I realize now that I was delirious. As the plane took off from the tarmac, my mom whispered in my ears the all too fa-miliar saying, "Whatever it is, will we figure it out." (At least, I think it was my mom. I cannot recall.) Even though my brain was ill, I still worried. "What if it is too late?"

59

I don't remember traveling from the airport, let alone changing into my pajamas the previous evening, but my dad's alarm blared early that next winter morning. In the past, I had thought every other doctor's visit would be the conclusion to my story, and I'd go back to my old self. I had believed I'd get help and that everything would return to "normal". I'd graduate high school, go on to college, and my life would be hunky-dory. Life gets in the way when you're busy making plans, they say - more like chronic illness gets in the way when you're busy living life.

We drove past a cemetery on our drive to The Gedroic Medical Institute that morning, and I remember wondering whether I would soon become a part of those sleeping souls, too. I turned my thoughts away and placed my faith in Dr. Gedroic—a doctor I knew nothing about and would be meeting for the first time in less than an hour.

My parents shuffled about the small room in silence. They had been agitated with each other for merely breathing up until the time we had to leave. My dad accused my mom of taking too long to shower, and my mom said my dad took too long to change, and then they lost their tempers and started to scream at each other. Tensions were running high.

During the walk from the parking lot to the elevator, tears streamed down my face. I sat in my wheelchair, nervous that this appointment would end like the rest: without an answer. My hands quivered from the touch of my mom's palm on my shoulder, and I immediately could feel her tense energy, too. She stopped pushing my chair and came around to the front of me and placed her hands on my knees. Her eyes were watery, and it seemed like she would burst with any sudden movement.

I asked her, "What if she says I'm not ill, like the rest?"

She replied, "If so, we will continue to do what we have been doing and keep going."

When we walked into the building, the facility manager es-corted us back to Dr. Gedroic's office. I should have known that I was in good hands when one of the nurses helped me walk back to the examination room. Instead, however, my apprehen-sion ran high. The feeling of safety didn't fully encapsulate me until Dr. G began her examination. She bent down and whispered to me, "I promise, I am going to help you." Though my brain was foggy, and my teeth were incessantly chat-tering because of neurological deficits, somewhere, I developed tears. But this time, I cried because of a feeling I thought I had long ago lost the capacity to feel—joy.

I was told about these details later, after several treatments because when I went to Dr. Gedroic's office originally, I was severely neurologically impaired. What I do remember from that first appointment was that Dr. Gedroic walked into the room, shook my hand, looked me in the eyes, and said, "Wow, you have quite the story." The first time in over two years, a doctor had acknowledged me, and more importantly, validated me.

ONE   WEEK   LATER

We returned to her office, traveling up the steep walkway to the doors of the professional building. My parents' heads were downcast as they pushed me along the long corridor towards the elevator. I didn't know what to think. We had traveled down this

road several times before only to be let down by the lack of find-
ings in my results.

He stood next to me as we rode the elevator to the third floor,
clutching my hand as tears fell from my cheeks. He wore his
tuxedo and black dress shoes as always. To this day, it still makes
me laugh. I don't know why I placed faith in this man who initially tried to kill me. But he was the only one who had indeed
witnessed it all, throughout the two-year ordeal. He was a constant in a time of upheaval.

When the elevator doors opened, it felt as if we were all moving in slow motion. He walked beside me, and my mom was
pushing my chair as my dad went ahead to open the front door
of Dr. Gedroic's facility. The twenty yards or so from the
eleva-tor to the front door felt like miles. Though my
vision was blurry, I suddenly saw something. I leaned forward,
feeling the warmth emitted by the blurry spectacle. As I moved
closer, the warmth filled every vein of my being until all I saw
was white light.

* * * * *

"Lauren, you're in liver failure, and your gallbladder, pan-
creas, and kidneys are starting to shut down. You have seven
coinfections of Lyme, heavy metals, parasites, and toxic mold
poisoning."

According to her, I wouldn't have lived to make it to the August 27th appointment.

I wasn't crazy, and it wasn't my imagination - he was right. I
was dying. The only question that remained was, how do I know
this treatment will save me?

15 MONTHS LATER...

Two steps were all that hindered me from receiving my diploma. Standing on the risers in my cap and gown, I thought back to my journey and how far I came. I almost died, and yet, here I was, one name call away from being a high-school graduate.

After the follow-up appointment, my health took a turn for the worse. The dosage of the medication, although tolerated by most, was something I couldn't handle. My vision worsened, my neurological system imploded, and 100-degree-plus fevers became a daily occurrence. My family thought they had made the biggest mistake of their lives, and yet I felt safer than ever. I somehow knew, deep beyond the depths of illness, past the hallucinations of *Him,* somewhere secluded deep in my conscious, that I was in the care of a great physician. I'm not sure how, but I knew it to be true that I would return to being a "normal" girl. I still wasn't sure, however, of the degree to which I would be able to function.

I entered what the nurses called the "ICU" of the facility. Treatment consisted of IV's five days a week for four to eight hours at a time. Somedays, the treatment would last three hours, and the next might be five. I suffered side effects more debilitating than anything I could describe in writing, as it wouldn't do it justice. Fortunately, I did enjoy the ability to fall asleep quickly and deeply, which I hadn't experienced in over a year. Sleep allowed me to continue the fight each day by restoring the meager amount of strength left in me to endure each treatment.

In late June of 2018, my levels stabilized enough that my doctor felt comfortable to start the parasitic regimen. She thought that one or two rounds of the four medications would be sufficient to clear my system. I went through six. I remember snapshots in which I clutched the rim of a toilet bowl or in which I was paralyzed from my waist down. I remember my doctor saying that one of the drugs would be the worst of all because it tackled the neurological component; boy was she right.

He became more violent, and I suffered unique hallucinations (i.e., imagining bugs crawling up our apartment walls) and the inability to maintain posture or control of my body. My parents would reposition me so I wouldn't hit my head on objects or shelves when they were pushing me in my wheelchair. My mom said I would drool, and I had an obsession with playing with my fingers. Late in the summer of 2018, I was standing in the kitchen, holding onto the counter, when a wave of dizziness came over me. I grabbed the apple cider vinegar, which was, oddly enough, the only drink able to stop my nausea in its tracks. But before I could reach up and grab a glass, the feeling in my legs vanished, and I collapsed into my mom's arms.

With each round, my symptoms diminished in severity. By October, I was ready to start walking. One day per week, for about an hour, I used my wheelchair as a walker and took a stroll around the lobby of our apartment complex. My mom or dad would join me on my expedition, as I didn't know how long my legs would support me before they gave out from exhaustion. Some of my best memories are of the conversations we'd share while walking those halls.

My neurological illness had dissipated by late fall, and I was back to taking my three AP classes through virtual school. I remember the shock I felt when I began the new chapter in AP Statistics, and I grasped the material with such ease that I thought there was something wrong with me. I didn't have to use phonics cards to memorize the correct spelling of words—I understood formulas and facts with ease. I knew I loved to learn, but this newfound ability made me realize that enduring the treatment was worth it after all.

I started physical therapy and, by the end of January 2019, I walked through the airport with my wheelchair for balance and hopped on a flight back to Florida.

I did have some anxiety about returning to where all of my health problems had begun. Sure, the state did not make me ill, but the physicians only exacerbated my illness. My excitement rose as I would return to the school I still consider to be my second family: IMG. Without their support, I wouldn't have been able to put my studies on hold and walk with the graduating class this year. I consider my relationships with my teachers to be akin to that of close friends. Throughout my journey, our bond has deepened.

* * * * *

"Lauren Bacall Kingsly."

I took the two steps and started to walk across the stage towards my headmaster, but I turned and stopped to wave to my parents and my golf coach, Jay. This moment was for them. My ability to walk across this stage, ailment free, clear-minded, and ready to start the next chapter would not have been able to happen had it not been for their support. Memories of my coach chatting with me in the shade on the golf course and of my parents carrying me to the bathroom in the middle of the night, when I couldn't put any pressure on a single joint, flitted through my mind. I owed so much to all of them.

I shook Mr. Locke's hand, and we hugged. "I'm so proud of you," he whispered. I was pretty damn proud of myself, too. I walked a bit further and hugged Ms. Gubernat next. "You did it, hun," she whispered. Then, with a few more steps, I walked backstage, diploma in hand, ready for whatever other challenges life decides to throw my way.

Many people, including family members, friends, and fellow patients have told me they wished that I did not have to go through what I went through. Some have even asked, "What do you think would have happened to you had you not been chronically ill?"

I did not wish for my illness, but I'm thankful for the experience. The friendships I've made and the knowledge I've gained have allowed me to take care of myself and those around me.

To answer their question, I'm not sure what would have happened to me. But without my darkness, I would never have come to appreciate the light that is life.

THE END

Of this book, not my life.

ACKNOWLEDGEMENTS

Looking back, I realize that it took a village to help me reach the position I am in now. I am grateful to have a support team that caught me when I fell and tried relentlessly to help me back up. Lyme is an insidious disease that I'd never wish on my worst enemy, but without my experience, I wouldn't have found my passions. Through Lyme, I've come to learn of my love of writing and the study of parasitology. The latter is unique, but parasites are fascinating organisms. I'm happy to have harnessed this knowledge at an early age, and I'm excited to see where life takes me. Wherever I go, I know the following individuals will always be there, arms extended, ready to assist me in navigating life's many challenges:

Grandma and Grandpa Kingsly – Thank you for your unconditional love and for allowing me to follow my dreams. I'll love you always and forever.

IMG Academy faculty – I'll never forget your support and unwavering belief in my abilities, thank you for being my second family.

Coach Jay – Thank you for making the golf course a haven, your "philosophical" advice, and for never letting me be too stern.

Kelly Oaks – I'm beyond lucky to have had you as a teacher and now as a friend, thank you for your care and concern on my darkest days.

Lauren Beasley Shanaphy – To the best physical therapist to ever exist, thank you for helping me relearn to balance and unlocking my inner strength.

Amanda Ryan at CrossFit Veracity - Thank you for your constant support and for celebrating my small victories as if they were your own.

Dr. Rebecca Loomis – Thank you for your excellent navigation skills in life and illness; I am utterly grateful.

Lizzie Harbin – My fellow "Lyme buddy", thank you for the inspiration and advice. I'm thankful that fate and IVs brought us together.

Peter Klein – Thank you for your witty jokes and friendship; you never fail to make me laugh.

Gedroic Medical Institute Nurses – From drawing pictures on my IV bags to holding my hand during one of my "episodes," thank you for your constant care.

My sincerest gratitude,
Lauren Kingsly

About the Author

After spending two years battling Lyme Disease and finishing high school with honors, Lauren is spending her gap year continuing to recover and enjoying a healthy life. She takes long walks with her dog Carly, reads books on multiple topics, spends time with her family, and looks forward to a purposeful future. Writing her story solidified her desire to study English Literature with a focus on Creative Writing. Lauren's dream is to help others harness the power of their voice and build a strong team to celebrate the momentous day when they eradicate Lyme Disease.

Made in the USA
San Bernardino, CA
08 January 2020